Becoming A Parent

A Reality Check on Pregnancy, Birth, and Baby's First Year

Ann-Christin Villegas

Becoming A Parent

A Reality Check on Pregnancy, Birth, and Baby's First Year

© Copyright 2022, Ann-Christin Villegas

Library of Congress Control Number: 2022911569

Neither the author nor the publisher can be held responsible for the use of the information provided within this book. Please always consult a trained professional before making any decision regarding treatment of yourself or others.

This book only provides general information that may or may not apply to your personal health condition or circumstances. The opinions expressed in this book are strictly the authors own personal opinions and not the opinions or policies of any third party, including any health care provider, employer, educational or medical institution, professional association or charitable organization. Nothing in this book constitutes or shall be construed as constituting medical advice of any kind whatsoever; nor is it a substitute for professional medical advice, diagnosis and treatment.

There is no substitute for the relationship between a medical professional and his or her patient. See your treating physician, osteopath, nurse practitioner, midwife or other qualified healthcare provider regarding any questions you have about your personal health and any medical condition you may have, including a pregnancy. No information found in this book should be relied on or acted upon by you without first consulting your own treating healthcare provider. NEVER disregard professional medical advice or delay seeking it because of something you have read in this book. If you think you may have a medical emergency, call your doctor or 911 immediately. Reliance upon any information provided in this book is solely at your own risk.

For more information, email annchristinvillegas@gmail.com.

ISBN Print: 979-898614-182-4

GET YOUR FREE GIFT!

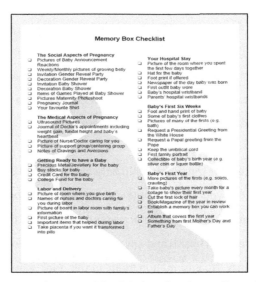

For the best experience with this book, I have found readers who download and use the Memory Box Checklist are able to collect more meaningful keepsakes they are able to pass on to their children.

You can get a copy by visiting:

https://mailchi.mp/cbc66cfa3102/becomingaparent

Dedication

I dedicate this book to my family. My wonderful husband and my two amazing daughters, with a future third child in mind! You have made me a better person, given me more self-confidence, and maxed out my patience. Without you, my life would not be complete, I would not know the true joy of being a mother, and I would have fewer wrinkles. I love you with all my heart. Thank you for everything.

Table of Contents

Introduction

When you find out you will be a parent, you realize you have no idea what you have gotten yourself into. You have heard the stories and seen the videos and pictures on social media. Everyone else makes it seem so easy: perfect families, perfect parents, and perfect babies. What does reality actually look like?

In this book, I am going to give you an overview of pregnancy, birth, and the first year of your baby's life. It is based on real life experiences with no sugarcoating included. You will find out many details you didn't know before and be better prepared for this special time in your life. This book is for anyone who wants to prepare themselves for what lies ahead on the journey to parenthood until their baby's first birthday. Get comfortable while you read this book and be open-minded. Take from this book what suits you best and ignore the rest. This book will not give you a scientifically proven way to raise your baby. This book is not for readers who want to learn about every single possible scenario on every topic.

Many of the examples mentioned in this book are based on my story – not a perfect story, not a horror story, but a true story. A story about the good, the bad, and the ugly of being pregnant, having a baby, and surviving (and thriving!) the first year of being a parent.

To contextualize my approach to the topics covered in this book, you need to understand my background a little bit more. I am a German immigrant to the United States who became a naturalized citizen. I met my American husband of Hispanic background in Germany, when he was stationed there with the US Army. We met when we were seventeen and eighteen years old, and have been together ever since. We lived in Germany for many years and got married there. Eventually, we moved to the United States and built our life here. As a Biotech Engineer with a Project Management certification (PMP), I surprisingly struggled quite a bit to find employment in my field. A foreign degree is not accepted everywhere, but I eventually settled into my current role as Operations Manager for a consulting company in the pharmaceutical industry.

We welcomed two amazing daughters who, from day one, gave us joy and happiness, as well as headaches and frustration. As first-time parents having none of our families around or any friends with little children close by, we had to figure things out on our own. I did much research to find out what to expect, what will happen, and how things work out. I had a very hard time finding good, real, raw information on all the topics of pregnancy, birth, and raising a baby. I often found myself getting lost in some blogs or chat rooms after researching one specific topic for over 30 minutes. After meeting other new parents and exchanging ideas and experiences, I learned they also encountered the same struggles. I got so frustrated about not finding real information easily and all in one spot, I decided to write this book to make it easier for everyone else who is becoming a parent.

That being said, this book is not a complete collection of everything that could possibly happen during this span of time. It is based on what I know and experienced myself, so certain topics like C-sections (I had both my girls vaginally), are not thoroughly covered in this book. I want to give you real information, not wrong information. I am not a doctor, a nurse, or a child development specialist. I am just a mother who truly cares about other parents and supporting them on their journey. I have been able to support and motivate friends and strangers around me -all new parents- giving me the motivation to reach a bigger audience.

I promise if you finish reading this book, you will either know better what to expect and how you want to raise your baby, or you will know exactly what you never want to implement with your baby. Either way is a win. You will have a better understanding of what is important to you, and can prepare yourself better for what lies ahead. Do not go into this journey thinking you already know everything. You will be surprised by how many questions you will have throughout your pregnancy, birth, and parenthood. This book will tell you the unembellished truth of what is coming your way, and will answer many of the questions you might already have.

The Social Aspects of Pregnancy

"There is no such thing as a perfect parent, so just be a real one." — Sue Atkins

I am 2½ years into motherhood and reading this quote makes me nod my head and say, "Oh Yes!" out loud. But let's start from the beginning.

My husband and I met in 2005, and after dating for six years, we got married in the Heidelberg Castle in Germany. It was our dream wedding and the start of our family. As soon as we announced our wedding plans, family and friends started asking when we were going to have children. Three years into our marriage we wanted to grow our family and tried having a baby. After a year, I finally got pregnant, and we immediately shared the great news with our families when I was pregnant in my fifth week. Two weeks later we had to give out the sad news I had miscarried. It was not only very sad for us that we couldn't grow the family as planned, but it was also horrible to tell all the family members, "never mind, there would not be an addition to the family after all." Don't get me wrong, everyone was very supportive and other women reached out to tell me they had gone through the same thing. Nevertheless, it did not make the experience easier at the time. I was very surprised to learn how many women in my extended family, and how many friends, had gone through the same experience. Unfortunately, this topic is still treated as a taboo when, in fact, this is a very common occurrence from what I have seen. We decided if this should happen again, we would not tell anyone. At least people around us didn't ask when we would finally have children.

Two years later, I got pregnant again and two weeks after finding out, the same thing happened again. We were very upset, but this time around we kept it between us. In 2017, we moved from Germany to the United States and started a new and exciting chapter of our lives in Northern Virginia.

Three months later, I got pregnant again. This time it seemed like things were going well. When I had my first ultrasound at 10 weeks, I found out there was no heartbeat and the fetus had only grown to seven weeks. Another disappointment, more tears shed, but at least we had each other. All tests we had done showed we were both healthy and should not have any issues having children. It was so frustrating not knowing what the problem was. Nothing made sense. It was an emotional rollercoaster and the three miscarriages left me feeling like I couldn't do the 'basic task' a woman should do: bear children.

Half a year later, the miracle finally happened: five long years and three miscarriages into our journey, we were finally expecting our first child. However, this time around we shared the news with our families and friends after 12 weeks; everyone was happy and relieved.

Trying to get pregnant or having a child is very different for everyone. Some start trying and get pregnant immediately; for others it takes more time. Some have miscarriages, some have twins or even triplets. For some, it doesn't happen without a little help like IUIs or IVFs. Some cannot have children and adopt while others have no partner, but still want children.

Whatever route it took you to get pregnant or to be expecting an addition to the family: Congratulations, you are part of the lucky ones!

Finding out you are going to have a baby is full of emotions. Those can be positive or negative. If you tried and wanted a baby, then the happiness is overwhelming. If you got pregnant and didn't want to, then the news can be devastating, and the decision has to be made to keep the baby or to terminate the pregnancy. This book will focus only on having the baby.

Once the news sinks in that you are expecting a baby and the initial happiness and excitement is over, other emotions can overwhelm: insecurities, self-doubt, and fear. Am I really ready to have a baby? Is this a good idea? How do I raise a child successfully? What do I need to do? How do I prepare? What if something happens during the pregnancy? What if the baby isn't healthy? Will I be a good parent?

This mix of emotions is totally normal and doesn't mean you are not ready. It just means you actually care and want to be the best parent you can be.

One of my brothers gave us the best advice we had heard to date when we told him: "Follow your instincts and do your best. When your children are 18 years old, they can tell you all the things you did wrong."

Now that you have processed the news and you may have had your first doctor's appointment where everything looked good, one of the fun moments of pregnancy is happening: the announcement to the people around you that you are expecting a baby. Usually, people will be very happy for you and excited. Enjoy seeing family and friends getting huge smiles on their faces and maybe some teary eyes. This is fantastic news! At the same time, this is somehow an unwritten, unofficial invitation for people to flood you with unsolicited advice. Be patient, they mean well and only want the best for you. Listen to what they say. Even if you know you don't want to use certain techniques, it is always good to know there are options out there other than what you want to do, because at one point you might be desperate for a different approach.

Some people consider the announcement as a free pass to start touching the mom's belly. This can be cute and loving from someone you know and care about. It is different if complete strangers walk up to you in the street and start treating your belly as a petting zoo. There is nothing wrong with setting boundaries and telling them, NO. Stand your ground. It doesn't matter if they feel offended. This is about YOU and YOUR body.

You might also encounter negative responses to your announcement from people who are, or were struggling with getting pregnant, or from people who cannot have children. Try not to take it personally. This is based more on their own unhappiness about their situation and emotional pain. It does not mean they are not happy for you. Either give them their space until they come around after they have processed their feelings so they can be happy for you, or simply move on. You do not need this negativity in your life. You will need the most support of the people around you.

Now that everyone knows you are pregnant, the next question is: are you having a boy or a girl? Some people want to know, some want it to be a surprise, and others decide to have a gender reveal party. This is often followed by a baby shower. People around you start asking about these events when you haven't even figured out what you actually want to do. You look around and suddenly find these huge and exaggerated events on social media and feel pressured to deliver something like what you see to meet a certain standard that is being set by people you don't even know.

Be careful not to get sucked into the fads that happen around you, but sit back and think about what it is you really want, and what makes more sense. Did you know before you even got pregnant you might have a gender reveal party? Awesome, go for it, enjoy it! There are so many beautiful ways to find out if you are having a boy or a girl that it can be very difficult to decide on the way you want to find out. If it seems too much for you, or you just don't really care about this option, then don't do it. No need to please other people.

The event usually done more often is a baby shower. This can be organized by you or by a friend. It can even be a surprise. My recommendation here is: truly enjoy the time you have with friends and family. Soon you will find it hard to enjoy a full day or even a half day of preparations and festivities, because the baby will need your full attention. People around you will want to give you gifts and the baby shower is a nice venue for that. Anyone who is invited is usually relieved if there is a baby registry, so try to get yours done before the baby shower. It allows your guests to gift you items you actually want and need, instead of guessing what you might want and giving you something you don't like or already have. It is also a great way to save some money. You will still spend enough of it here shortly. Looking for baby items can be loads of fun and exciting, but also very overwhelming.

There are so many options out there and some things are just unnecessary, but how would you know that? Ask parents around you what really helped them out or what they wouldn't want to miss, to find some things that might not be super cute but will help you out in the long run. Some of my registry favorites are the *Oogiebear* to dig out the buggers from the baby's nose and *Sock Ons* to keep those tiny baby socks on their feet. Otherwise, you see them fly through the air to disappear behind the changing table furniture. Another excellent option is a food delivery gift card you can use after you have the baby, on a crazy day when you cannot cook.

Another fun event during pregnancy is the maternity photo shoot. Pregnancy is such a special time of your life. It is beautiful to capture some moments in pictures, to look back and remember the times you thought everything was just amazing and beautiful. If the cost of a professional photographer is a concern, then ask a friend who is good at taking pictures. You can find many good poses and ideas online to prepare for it. Don't do it too early though; you want your belly to pop in the pictures. If you decide to go to special locations like monuments or national parks, find out if you need a permit to shoot pictures there to avoid a disappointing surprise and get turned away. When you take the pictures, enjoy yourself. It's another beautiful milestone during pregnancy and a very special time in your life.

If this is not your first child and you have older siblings attend the photo shoot, then this can all look a bit different, especially if one is a toddler. Scale down your expectations; they will not cooperate for a few hours to take nice smiley pictures. Take some with them and some without. If they cry a lot or just look angry because it's too hot or too cold, then accept it as it is. That is the best you will get. Everyone has these perfect pictures in their head, especially family pictures, but be ready to just accept pictures everyone is in, sometimes even with a sippy cup or snack in their hand, and embrace it. You will look back at those pictures

and chuckle. They still capture a very special day of your life and portray your life as it is. That is as good as it can get!

Enjoy the fun big events during your pregnancy, but there are other important things to prepare for that receive less fanfare, and one of them is taking care of yourself. Treat yourself a little bit, do something that makes you feel good, like a pedicure or a massage. Do something that takes time because you might not be able to do that anytime soon, for quite some time.

At the same time, don't overprepare and don't overspend. There are so many options for everything out there, and it is normal to want only the best for your child. Try to be reasonable and figure out what your baby actually needs versus what you want on top of that.

What your baby initially needs, besides you, is the following:

- a bassinet or crib for safe sleep,
- a car seat,
- a carrier or stroller,
- diapers and wipes,
- some clothes like onesies (short-sleeve and long-sleeve), socks, pants, hats, mittens (if your baby scratches themselves), pajamas, and,
- formula and bottles if you don't breastfeed.

Everything else can wait. The baby won't care if there is a fully set up nursery or playroom yet. You might even find out room setups don't actually work well and make no sense once the baby is there, compared to how you envisioned it. Make additions over time instead of putting everything up before the baby is born.

Focus on the safety areas like a new car seat to ensure it has never been in a car accident that compromised its safety features. You can get an appointment with your local police or fire department to get the installation of the car seat checked to make sure the baby will be safe in the car. Invest in a good crib that ensures safe sleep for the baby. There are options for cribs that grow with your child and turn into toddler beds and eventually into full twin beds. Spend some time baby proofing your house, at least in the rooms where your baby will spend the most time. After that, lie down on your belly and look around you to find additional hazards for your baby at their eye level. Consider gates for stairs. Do you know another parent who can come to your house to check if there is anything else you need to adjust to keep the baby safe?

Before you become a parent, there are a few more things you can do to be ready for the baby. Number one is to enjoy couples time. Focus on each other and go out for a romantic dinner or take a short trip somewhere to have some relaxing quiet time together.

Try to prepare some meals you can put in the freezer so when you come back from the hospital, you have some time to settle in without having to worry about what you will eat for lunch or dinner. Have some nonperishable ingredients in the kitchen to easily cook something without having to run to the store. That extra hour you save is precious. If friends ask you how they can help, ask them to bring you meals.

Something else to consider is child care, if you already have a child. Once it is time to go to the hospital, you don't want to figure out where your child can stay for the time of your hospital stay. It's always good to have a Plan A and Plan B for backup, as this is so important. Do you have family around who can help? If not, any friends? Does your child care provider offer emergency stays over night? Make sure a bag is packed for your child with essentials like pajamas, toothbrush and toothpaste, diapers and wipes if still needed, favorite toys, clothes, water bottle, and a snack.

Speaking of packing bags: don't forget to pack your own! You will not need three suitcases for your 2 - 3 days' stay, assuming everything goes well at the hospital. Find out what the hospital supplies to patients. Ours supplied a gown for myself with easy access for breastfeeding, socks, sheets, a toothbrush and toothpaste for me; towels, and bedding for the partner. On top of that, I received everything I needed to take care of myself. We only needed to pack the basics, like clothes for all three of us to go back home and some more toiletries we wanted to use from our own supply. I also packed a few sanitary pads-the thickest ones I could find- for the bleeding after giving birth because I did not want to leave the hospital in the net underwear they

provided. Make sure to pack a phone charger or other chargers for any electronics you want to take. Your favorite snack is also nice to eat in between everything that is going on, and then whatever else you can think of that will help you out during your stay there. Some women like to have certain scents during labor or certain lights. Just check with your hospital if you can bring whatever it is you decide on, if it is not one of the standard items.

Finally, think about collecting some memories from this special time in your life. It can be nice to look back at them a few years down the line to trigger forgotten memories, or just as a gift for your children when they get older and ask about your pregnancy with them. There are many little details one can collect like the baby shower invite, some nice decorations from the celebration, or other items that were meaningful to you during this time, such as healing stones, for example.

At the end of each chapter, you will find a Memory Box with ideas of what you can collect from these specific time periods. There will also be some blank lines where you can write down any ideas that pop up as you read this book, so you don't forget them later on. I have collected many small mementos for both of my daughters and ordered a nice folder to put them in. I will give it to them on their 18th birthday. I hope it will be meaningful to them, especially when they start their own families.

While reading this first chapter, you probably wondered why I didn't talk about important topics like symptoms during pregnancy or ultrasounds. This chapter specifically focused more on the social aspects of pregnancy, whereas the medical aspects of pregnancy can be found in the following chapter.

Memory Box

Invitation Gender Reveal Party

Decoration Gender Reveal Party

Invitation Baby Shower

Decoration Baby Shower

Items of Games Played

Pictures of Maternity Photoshoot

Pictures of Baby Announcement Reactions

Monthly/Weekly Pictures of Your Belly Growth

Pregnancy Journal

Your Favorite Shirt

_____

_____

_____

_____

_____

The Medical Aspects of Pregnancy

In the previous chapter, we talked about the social and emotional aspects of pregnancy. I hope you already have some ideas of memories to collect and noted those in writing. Now let's focus more on the medical aspects of pregnancy.

My first pregnancy was overall 'easy' compared to others. I was nauseous for seven weeks; I had cravings for fruit and chocolate and was disgusted by chicken. I couldn't even watch a KFC commercial on TV without feeling sick! I was tired, but I took my naps, took care of myself, and honestly, I had never lived this healthy in my life! I was not working at the time and could just focus on myself and the baby. Having gone through three miscarriages before, I wanted this pregnancy to work out. I felt like I needed to protect my body from the physical and mental stress of my prior employments, not knowing if this contributed to my body rejecting the pregnancies.

The pregnancy with my second baby was very different. After my older daughter's first birthday, we tried for a second baby and I immediately got pregnant again. This time around I was working full time, and outside work I chased after my daughter. I had nausea again and my cravings. I was very tired and exhausted and overall, more stressed out. My belly grew bigger much faster, I felt the weight so much more, and I was more uncomfortable.

Towards the end of my second pregnancy, my daughter outran me while I tried keeping up with my waddles! I had lots of practice contractions, also known as Braxton Hicks contractions. They are mild contractions that, for me, felt like my belly was tightening, almost like flexing all my abdominal muscles without actually doing it or wanting to. I could hardly wait to be done with the pregnancy; it was literally the opposite of my first pregnancy.

The first giveaway you are pregnant usually is you miss your period, followed by a positive pregnancy test. Other clues for your being pregnant could also be implantation bleeding, almost like a light 1-day period, nausea, sore breasts, or fatigue, to name a few. That is when the first excitement kicks in. Followed by the question: And now what? What is the next step?

I was surprised with my pregnancies when I had visual confirmation from the tests indicating I was pregnant, as I did not feel pregnant at all. Everything seemed normal, so... was I really pregnant? Where were all the symptoms everyone always talked about?

I called the doctor's office immediately to share the news and to schedule my first appointment. Before I got my appointment, I had to do a urinary test to confirm the pregnancy. Once the results came back, I was finally able to schedule the appointment. The first appointment often does not get scheduled until 8 to 10 weeks after the first day of your last period. With my history of miscarriages, I was seen sooner, at about six weeks of pregnancy.

It was an ultrasound to verify the fetus was alive. I was a nervous wreck. For both of my babies there was a heartbeat, and it was an immense relief to know everything was fine at that point. During the first 'regular' appointment, you go over your medical history with your doctor to find out if there are any genetic predispositions or other factors, like your lifestyle, that might have negative effects on your baby's health. Examples are smoking and drinking alcohol, diabetes, or other diseases. You also get weighed to set a baseline to check if you gain weight properly, and if you are lucky, you get to peek at your baby for the first time.

During pregnancy, mothers want to make sure their baby is healthy and developing properly. The best way to do this is to take care of yourself, go to all your doctor's appointments, and listen to your doctor's advice implicitly. That includes not only your routine checkups, but also going to the dentist and getting a dental cleaning. Some insurances even offer an additional free cleaning during pregnancy. While pregnant, you have a greater risk of tooth decay and gingivitis. Gingivitis is a mild form of gum disease, and if left untreated can develop into a serious gum disease. This can be harmful to you and your baby, possibly leading to preterm birth.

All that being said, I think it is best to be realistic about how you take care of yourself. There is the aspect of nutrition; what to eat, how many times, of course what NOT to eat because it could harm your baby, what to drink or not to drink, and also exercise.

My first pregnancy symptoms started showing up with my first baby at five weeks, with my second one at seven weeks. I was very nauseous, had cravings and aversions. So yes, I tried sticking to the advice of what to eat and how much of it, but if the first spoon of oatmeal makes you throw up, you might not keep down the food you want to eat. Initially, I ate very little and always the same things, so I felt like I didn't get the nutrients I needed. I took my prenatal vitamins, which helped, but sometimes my dinner consisted of a big plate of fruit with chocolate. Of course, the chocolate was not a healthy option, but I really wanted it, and it tasted so delicious I simply could not resist! No, I did not eat an entire bar of chocolate, just a few pieces to satisfy my craving, but in the end, it stayed down, and I was happy.

So yes, it is good to try and live healthy, but it is very unlikely you can go the entire pregnancy without cheating once in a while, and that's ok. I don't know anyone who was pregnant, who never ate something that was unhealthy. Just try not to let this be anywhere near the biggest portion of your diet. When you talk to your doctor at the beginning of your pregnancy, you will discuss what a healthy weight gain for you is over the following weeks and months. Should you feel like your weight gain is too accelerated, or you are not sure what the best plan is for you, your doctor can give you more tips on nutrition or you can consult a dietitian who can customize a nutrition plan for you. If you have always been a thin or petite person, the immense weight gain can be difficult to accept, especially when you think about having to lose those 20 or 30+ pounds again. It can feel a little bit overwhelming. Watching the numbers for your weight go up consistently can scare you away from the scale. Should you experience this, talk to your doctor about not sharing the weight numbers with you, but letting you know if your weight gain is fine, or if perhaps you need to adjust your diet.

Another topic is exercise during pregnancy. Of course, it is healthy to exercise, and you should try to get some exercise every day. This does not have to be lifting weights or running. Usually, the women who do these types of exercises are already very fit and this was part of their routine before they got pregnant. Pregnancy is not the time in your life to start a new challenging sport like tennis or soccer. If you have done minor sports before you got pregnant, stick to them, and going for walks, swimming, or yoga is a great way to get some exercise without harming your body. Do not feel badly because you see these other moms doing extensive fitness routines while you can barely get out of bed. Do what you can, and what you have time for.

During my first pregnancy, I went swimming three times a week and for walks every day. I didn't work, so I had the time. When I was pregnant with my second child, I worked full time, but before and after work, it was family time with my husband and daughter. The bigger I got, the faster my daughter ran. In the end my waddles could not keep up with her, but she kept me on my feet and that was my exercise. All these topics can be discussed with your doctor to make sure you are taking care of yourself the right way, without overdoing it and exposing yourself or your baby to any risks.

Besides the nausea, other symptoms during pregnancy for me were fatigue, headaches, nosebleeds, back pain, and practice contractions. Sleeping at night with a huge belly was also not very easy, so I would usually wake up four to five times a night to turn around to the other side. So, overall, not too bad compared to other women's stories I heard all around me. Everyone experiences different symptoms. One of my friends had no symptoms at all during her three pregnancies. She said if it wasn't for her growing belly and the baby moving, she wouldn't have known she was pregnant! I had a classmate at college who was sick the entire time until she gave birth. One of my friends had really swollen ankles, another one had gestational diabetes. As I said, everyone has different symptoms, and the severity differs as well. I know some people say the more nauseous you are, the stronger the pregnancy is, and the lesser the risk of losing the baby. Or if you have a certain belly shape (that only they can see) it will be a girl or a boy. Don't listen to these wives' tales. Everyone experiences these symptoms differently and just because someone else's symptoms start earlier or seem stronger, doesn't mean that your pregnancy will be more difficult or problematic.

So, try not to compare your experiences to anyone else's. If you are one of the lucky ones with the lesser evil symptoms, just be happy and enjoy your pregnancy. Do not question why you are part of the lucky ones, just embrace it. You could also be part of the unluckier ones who get preeclampsia. This is a potentially dangerous pregnancy complication. Signs are high blood pressure, swelling in the legs, blurred vision, and usually starts after twenty weeks. Sometimes it can be difficult to distinguish between normal symptoms like swollen ankles. I didn't have it, but the mothers I know who did just really listened to their bodies and their gut instincts to know something wasn't right, so they went to have it checked out. Some got cleared with either not having it, or if they did, to keep an eye on it; for others it was more acute, and they were monitored in the hospital. You know your body best. Whenever you feel like something is wrong or something doesn't feel right, or you think your baby isn't moving as much as it should, make an appointment to see your doctor immediately. Trust your 'Mom gut.' The best thing that can happen is they tell you your feelings tricked you and everything is ok. If something does come up, it is best to catch it as early as possible.

Something else to not compare is the belly size and shape. I did not know there were so many different belly shapes during pregnancy. I was very thin with my first one, only gaining nineteen pounds, and I only got bigger on my belly. Nothing on my legs or arms; I was really lucky. I felt huge, and I felt the weight, but I still looked much thinner than most other pregnant women around me. My first baby was born at 7 lbs. 12 oz. Great. With my second one, my belly was the same size at seven months as it was when I gave birth to my first. Of course, I kept growing and growing. I was afraid my second daughter would be too big for a natural child birth. In the end, I also only gained nineteen pounds and she was born at 7 lbs 8 oz. So yes, looks can be deceiving. My nurse told me the belly is like a balloon. The first time you inflate a balloon, it is a little difficult and more resistant. Every additional time you blow up the balloon afterwards, it's easier and easier. That stuck with me.

A very nice and exciting part of pregnancy are the ultrasounds and the first glimpses you get to see of your baby. Ultrasounds are usually done for medical reasons, so I was surprised to see how few ultrasound pictures I received during my pregnancy. I assumed that whenever I had an appointment, I would also get an ultrasound done, but that was simply not the case. At several appointments, I got my belly measured with a measuring tape for the fundal height; and if it checked out, all was well. With my second baby, I measured smaller a few times and had to get extra ultrasounds to make sure the growth was on target. Luckily everything came back just fine. Of course, I would have preferred getting the ultrasound done at every appointment to not have these questions pop up. If you feel like you want more pictures of your baby, especially in 3D, 4D or as of this moment, even 5D, and are willing to pay for them out of pocket, then there are more options. We chose 3D for our first and 4D for our second baby, and for us it was amazing to see them in such sharp quality before they were born. For us, it was magical. Others don't care about these offers and would just rather wait until they meet their baby in person. Do whatever feels comfortable for you as a couple.

Another crazy aspect of pregnancy are the out-of-control hormones. Pregnancy is full of ups and downs, mood swings, and intense emotions. You will have good days and bad days. It is easier to deal with these mood swings when both partners are aware of it. On bad days, you don't even know why you are upset or in a bad mood. I once cried because I spilled a glass of water. What usually is no big deal, was really horrible for me at that moment. You might get really frustrated and angry for no good reason and that, topped with the feeling of being very huge and uncomfortable, maybe even in pain, is a bad combination. I am a very reasonable and logical person and I was fully aware this was happening to me, and still, I couldn't seem to control it. My husband and I were having dinner once, and I started to cry. When he asked me what was wrong, I could only answer it was my hormones because there was literally nothing that had happened to make me upset. I had a great day, dinner was delicious, and I was excited to have a baby soon.

The best for me was that my husband was very understanding and didn't take it personally. He was there for me when I needed to talk or gave me my space when I just had to get myself under control. Partners can help out tremendously with reaffirming, nice words, and by not taking things personally. Pregnant women can say many harsh things, but they usually don't mean them the way they say it. It just comes out wrong, fueled by unexplainable emotions, and no one likes to admit they are wrong. It might be easier to pretend it is your partner's fault instead of owning your mistake and apologizing to them. When the moms-to-be do apologize though, just accept it, drop it and move on. There is nothing worse for a pregnant woman than being miserable, making that step towards their partner, then being pushed back.

For partners, it can be very difficult to understand what pregnant women are going through. If you haven't experienced it yourself, it is hard to accept that a towel folded the 'wrong' way can almost mean the end of the world in this situation. To the partners: please try to be understanding and extra patient. Self-reflection on both sides can be helpful and deescalate bad situations. If you need a break, then take one. Sometimes it is better to cool off for a few minutes before talking about the situation. Try to keep in mind the hormonal outbursts are only temporary.

Besides staying physically healthy, it is also very important to stay mentally healthy. All these changes to the body and hormones can cause friction in a relationship. For some women, it is difficult to accept their bodies are changing so much. Sometimes partners are not attracted to a pregnant woman with a huge belly, and in some cases, partners can grow apart as a result. It is important when you notice issues are coming up to talk about them. If you don't feel comfortable talking to each other about them, then find a third party resource to help out. This could be a friend, your doctor, a psychologist, other pregnant women in the same situation, or any other support network you can find. For both of my pregnancies I was seen in a Military installation, and I was part of a Centering group. This is a group of eight to ten pregnant

women who are all due in the same month. It was great to be able to connect with others who were going through the same thing, and for the partners as well. It is always reassuring to know you are not the only one struggling with certain experiences or topics, but that it is all normal and just part of the journey.

While you are doing a great job staying healthy and going to your doctor's appointments, it is also important to plan ahead for giving birth. Make sure to find a hospital you like to deliver your baby. Is the clinic where you are seen also a place where you can and would want to have your baby? Look around where there are hospitals and do a tour to get a good feel for what it is like, what to expect, and if you can see yourself giving birth there. Once you find a place you like, find out if you can pre-register to avoid paperwork when it is showtime. That way, you don't have to remember your first day of your last period, or social security number when you are in labor and about ready to give birth on the spot! Then find a backup hospital you can go to in case your first choice is at full capacity and cannot accept more patients. Some things to consider are the capabilities of the clinic in case something goes wrong (emergency C-section or an infection), or the baby needs further immediate attention (access to a NICU), if there are lactation consultants on site, if the baby can stay in your room, and if your partner can sleep over as well.

Start thinking about a birth plan and see if this is something you would like to put together or not. It is a collection of your wishes and intentions for the labor process so the nurses can support you in the best way possible. Once those contractions kick in and you are in major pain, you might forget some details or important decisions, so it is wise to have something written down that the nurses can read and accommodate.

Speaking of contractions: starting as early as week twenty of your pregnancy, you can get practice contractions. I was lucky to not get them until later; with my first baby around thirty-seven weeks, with my second one around thirty-two weeks. To me, they felt like my belly was flexing without me doing anything. They weren't terribly painful, just awkward and not controllable. When they started, I took it easy and rested a bit, to not push myself too much and cause the contractions to get worse. Towards the end of my second pregnancy, they got more uncomfortable. I had them every day, the whole day, and they hurt a little bit. There were a few days I actually thought this might be the real deal, but then they went away. If you can go to bed at night and fall asleep and don't wake up from crazy pain, it's probably not real contractions, but you never know. When you can't wait to get done with the pregnancy, you almost wish these contractions are the real ones starting your labor, but eventually you will know they are just the practice ones because you get over them and they remain the same or go away.

Towards the end of your pregnancy, you will feel much heavier, and experience greater pain. When you are working, this can be an enormous challenge. If you have a job where you need to be on your feet the whole day, it can seem impossible to get through the day. If you have a desk job, it can be brutal to sit down the whole day. When you get to a point where your normal work routine is not sustainable, talk to your employer to see what changes can be made to support your wellbeing, and ultimately the baby's health. Some women power through and go into labor at work; for others their health will not allow that. If necessary, take sick leave before your delivery. See how you feel, but do not feel pressured into overdoing it; the most important thing is the baby is doing well. If you feel like it is too much, get a doctor's note. There is no need to prove anything to anyone.

You went through three trimesters of pregnancy and can't wait to be done with it and finally meet your baby. Being pregnant and getting ready for the baby is exciting, but don't forget this is not all fun and games. You are adding another member to the family who will be completely dependent on you for hopefully, only eighteen years! In the next chapter, we will look at some added responsibilities.

Memory Box

Ultrasound Pictures

Pictures of your Growing Belly

Journal of Doctor Appointments Stating Weight Gain, Fundal Height and Baby's Heartbeat

Picture of Support Group or the Nurse/Doctor Caring for you

Notes of Cravings and Aversions

_____

_____

_____

_____

_____

_____

_____

Getting Ready to Have a Baby

The last two chapters talked about pregnancy, and we just covered some of the medical aspects you might experience during this time. You are probably ready to find out more about the scarier parts of the motherhood journey: labor and delivery. Before we get there, I want to take time to tell you more about some topics that seem rather dry, and can be more uncomfortable to talk about. They are equally important for the well-being of the family and peace of mind, so I recommend you stick through this one.

My husband and I focused on our careers while we were waiting to finally get pregnant. After some years in Germany, we moved to the US with our two cats. We initially rented an apartment to find out which areas were nice to live in, as we both were new to Northern Virginia. Six months later, we bought a house, and we enjoyed the freedom of traveling, just hopping on a plane for a long weekend, or Friday after work to explore more of the US. When we found out we were finally expecting our first baby, we needed to shift the focus on what would be best for us in the future, without compromising our values and what we loved doing most.

At this point, the reality had sunk in that it is not only you and your partner anymore, but there is a baby coming your way, who fully depends on you and the choices you make over the next few years.

A very important, but often neglected aspect to take into consideration is your finances. Ongoing expenses are no mystery, as you already know how much you pay for rent or mortgage, groceries, gas, other bills like electricity and water, phone, internet, and all the others that pile up. You budget your month around those bills. Now comes a new family member. How does that actually change the equation?

Some people think having a baby and raising a child is so expensive, it is out of their budget. This thought is usually an exaggeration. With proper planning and budgeting, you can set your family up for success. Other people say babies don't cost much because they don't need anything, but that is also not entirely true. Before your baby is born is a good time to consider some expenses that are coming your way and start planning and budgeting. That way, you can still enjoy everything you have done before and don't have to adjust too much.

You will have some immediate upfront expenses like the car seat, the bassinet or crib, the stroller, clothes, and everything else you need for your initial setup. Some of these items are very sophisticated and can come at a high price. Start thinking about what you actually need versus what you would like, but is not necessary. You don't have to buy everything at the same time; some things can wait. Some things you can find second hand; babies grow so fast they hardly get much use of certain things like clothes, or they quickly outgrow them. Hand-me-downs are also a great way to save money. They might not always be the cutest clothes you would choose for your baby, but your baby won't care, and they will only wear them for a few weeks before moving on to the next size. A great way to also save money is to have your baby registry ready so friends and family can gift you items you actually need, and would otherwise have to buy for yourself. Find out which baby registries offer a welcome box with samples to get a feel for what is out there and what you like. For my two baby registries, I chose Amazon because once you had your baby shower and people bought gifts for you, the leftover items on the registry receive a ten percent closeout discount.

Besides the immediate costs, there will be ongoing costs to keep in mind. The most obvious one is diapers and wipes. This will go on until they are potty trained, roughly around age three. Try different samples to see which ones work best for you. I like Huggies and Kirkland from Costco. Both brands are sold in Costco and as an added bonus, both brands go on sale once in a while. If you can save about $9 a box on Huggies, that is quite a bit of money you save over time. We buy several boxes of different sizes when there is a sale. If we don't use one, we can return it and get a refund.

Another option is cloth diapering. You can either do it yourself or sign up for a service for pickup of dirty diapers, cleaning, and drop off of clean diapers. I have not done the math on what makes more sense financially, but for me it was a choice of convenience and being more independent of a service, especially when traveling. Another ongoing cost if you are not breastfeeding is the formula, until they are about one year old. You can get free samples here and there, but overall, it is not an item that goes on sale very often. Babies are messy, so you will also do more laundry and see an increase in the water bill. Once they start eating solid foods, around six months of age, you need to buy more food for them. Find out if you are eligible for the WIC program, which helps with groceries. Babies and children grow like weeds, so you need to buy clothes much more often for them than for yourself.

A huge expense that shocked me was childcare. From what I have heard, the Washington, DC area where we live is on the pricier side more so than other areas. For our in-home daycare, we are spending $275 per week (!!) including a discount because our second daughter will start soon, plus a yearly activity fee, plus the initial sign-up fee. There are other daycares close by that charge around $350 to $500 a working week. This brings up a whole new question: Is it worth going back to work? I know women who quit their jobs and stay home because the paycheck after taxes would not cover the daycare cost, or they just broke even so they would rather stay home with their children. Others have the support of family members who can care for the children so they can go back to work. Try to find out the average childcare cost in your area to get an understanding of what makes the most sense for you. Other options if they are financially possible for you are nannies, shared nannies, or au pairs.

At this point, it is quite obvious that children cost you an arm and a leg over time, until they can provide for themselves. To set them up for success later on in their lives, you can look into getting them a credit card when they are born, which is connected to your own account. That way, you can already build up their credit score without them even knowing about it. If they need to take out a student loan or a loan for a car, they have a higher credit score, which will be a great help to them. Another option is a college fund, such as the tax-friendly 529 Plan. Every little bit can help them out when it is time for them to leave the house. This can cover costs that otherwise might come back to them in debt, or to you, when it might not be the best time to spend too much money all at once.

The financial aspect is probably the most important and immediate one. The next topic is one most people don't want to talk about, and rather not prepare their family for. What is the plan if something happens to you and your partner? When you are young and celebrating bringing a new life into the world, it might not seem like the right time to think about your own demise. Try to see it as time and money invested once now, so you don't have to worry about it again for a few decades, to bring you peace of mind. You never know what will happen and the last thing you want is for your children not to be taken care of, or end up in a place you least want for them. One thing I have observed is if there is no Will, the death of a family member brings out the worst in people. Most importantly, a Will gives you the chance to decide who will care for your children if you suddenly are no longer there, and what happens to your assets. We adjusted our Will before our first child was born and phrased it so it covers all future children as well. We could list the important items we own and decide who gets what and what happens with each asset. We could specify the age our children would get access to certain items, like jewelry or money. Sure, it felt weird talking about our death and it broke my heart thinking about not seeing my children grow up, but it was an exercise that needed to be done to protect our children in the worst situation possible. Hopefully, they will never see this version of the Will, and when they are old enough to care for themselves, we can adjust it again. Once you are looking into your Will, you can also explore life insurance. Some are offered through an employer, and some are offered privately. Does life insurance actually make sense for you? That depends on rates and personal financial situations. Do some research to decide for or against it.

If life insurance is offered through the employer, it is usually very affordable and some are even offered without the employee having to pay for it. Now is also a good time to find out from your employer (HR) what benefits will need to be updated with a new dependent, what the deadlines are (how much time after birth do you have to make the changes), and what paperwork you need to submit to make the changes. An important benefit is the health care plan, which often means the cost gets increased when adding a new family member. Many employers offer a dependent Flexible Spending Account (FSA), which gives you the chance to use $5,000 of your yearly income as tax free money to pay for childcare or summer camps.

For the mothers, it is important to find out about FMLA, which is twelve weeks of maternity leave that guarantee your job security while you take off to give birth, recover, and bond with your child. It is important to know that, in most states, this time is not paid. The way to get paid during this time is usually covered through Short Term Disability (STD) and does not have to be your full paycheck. I had six weeks of STD. The first two weeks I did not receive any money, so I could cover that with sick leave and PTO (Paid Time Off), and the other four weeks, it was a reduced amount of money. The following six weeks I stayed home with my baby unpaid. It took some planning ahead financially to make sure we could still cover all expenses, but for us, luckily it was possible. Every company offers a different plan, so make sure to find out what you can expect. You do not want to have to work this out while you are already staying home with the baby, trying to figure out how to keep this little human happy and your household intact!

One more topic to discuss with your partner before the baby arrives is how you actually want to raise your child. It is very important for both parents to be on the same page with the fundamental aspects of what you want to do, and, more importantly, what you don't want to do. My husband and I had very different upbringings. His family of Mexican background struggled financially when he was a young child. My German family was upper middle class. We both knew what we didn't want our children to have to go through or experience, and what values we wanted to instill in them. To get to an agreement on what we wanted for them, and how we would get them there, took some heated discussions and compromise. Now we both know what the best decisions for the family are and we don't undermine or contradict each other in front of our children.

Another unpopular topic to be discussed is the possibility of postpartum depression. This can happen with fathers as well as mothers, even though it is way more common for mothers. Talk about what signs to look for, and a game plan for how to address it, and the next steps. It is better to have a plan before the baby arrives and both parents are sleep deprived. Talk to your doctor about what to look for and when to seek help. Unfortunately, many people see postpartum depression as something shameful, or as a sign of weakness, and would rather hide it than seek treatment. That is not how you can be the best parent to your baby. Never let your pride get in the way of your well-being, thus the baby's well-being.

Overall, you need to decide what makes sense for you and your family, and don't be afraid to discuss these topics and other difficult topics not mentioned here with your partner. This is not only about you anymore, this is now about your children and family. As long as you remain respectful towards each other, and keep the goal of taking care of your children the best way possible in mind, there should be no reason why you could not discuss these topics with your partner. The best way to ensure success for your family is to be on the same page and make decisions on the important topics together.

Now that you are ready and prepared (so you think!) to meet the baby, let's take a look at the big event that stands between you now, and you holding the baby in your arms: giving birth.

Memory Box

Buying Precious Metal/ Jewelry for the Baby (Silver Coins, Gold Bars, and so on)

Buying a Stock for the Baby

Credit Card for the Baby

College Fund for the Baby

_____

_____

_____

_____

_____

_____

_____

_____

_____

Labor and Delivery

You have made it through the driest and most preparational part of the book. Now it is time to get to the painful part: labor and delivery. It is probably the scariest part of the journey as well, but you are mightily rewarded by holding your baby in your arms, so in the end, it is beyond well worth it. If you have not already done so, go ahead and ask your parents how your own birth went, if you want to hear some fun stories!

My mother had quick births. She didn't realize she was in labor because as discussed earlier, sometimes it is difficult to distinguish between the practice contractions in the beginning, or the real contractions. She thought she had practice contractions when she was actually going into labor. With all of us, we apparently could not wait to come out. When she had me, her water broke in the middle of a conversation with the neighbor. After my brothers were dropped off with the neighbors, my parents drove about thirty minutes to the hospital. My mother just made it into the hospital, where the staff reacted quickly by throwing a mattress on the floor because she didn't make it to the bed! Moments later, there I was, forty-five minutes after her water broke.

Of course, I was extremely concerned this would happen with my deliveries as well. I was afraid I wouldn't make it to the hospital if my husband had to drive home thirty minutes from work to pick me up, then get me to the hospital. Although our hospital was only fifteen minutes away in a Military installation, it was still concerning and hopefully there wouldn't be too much traffic at the gate to go in.

Turns out it was quite the opposite for both of my daughters. With my first one, I thought on a Friday evening my water had broken and I was leaking a little. We took everything to the hospital with us. My water had not broken, but the amniotic fluid was low enough for the doctors to induce me. This felt very planned and organized, so it was a little bit surreal for me. Eight hours into labor, I asked for an epidural and I couldn't get it fast enough. Initially, I wanted to have a natural birth if possible, and only request an epidural if I really had to, and could not handle the pain anymore. Trust me, I happily received the epidural! Afterwards, I was finally able to rest a little bit and sleep a couple hours before giving birth. When I actively started pushing, it took forty-five minutes until my daughter came out. With my second one, my contractions got worse on the 4th of July, and I was in pain the whole day. In the evening, after tucking our older one into bed at our friends' house, we left for the hospital. I had to walk around some more and climb some stairs before I was admitted.

To make sure I was healthy, I had to get a Covid test done. It felt like someone was punching me in my eye and brain; it was horrible. At the same time I had a contraction and the nurse followed this up by poking the IV needle into my arm. At this point, I requested the epidural again. Three hours later, they broke my water, and the baby sank down very quickly. They told me they would check in on me one or two hours later, but if I felt any pressure, I should let them know. Ten minutes later, past 2am, when my husband had finally fallen asleep, I woke him up again and called the nurse. The baby was on her way out. When everyone came rushing into the room to get the delivery going, I pushed for about five minutes and there she was, 2:25am on July 5th.

Every delivery is different, even for the same mother. The topics covered in this chapter are what I have personally experienced, and these deliveries were without issues.

When it is time for you to go to the hospital, it is a very emotional and scary moment. It doesn't matter if it is a planned C-section and you know exactly what time you have to show up there, or if it is whenever your body surprises you with contractions or water breaking. Once it hits you, you might get scared. A C-section is a surgery, the 'normal/vaginal' birth is very painful. Either way, you start questioning yourself if you can really do it? All the preparation you have done to date, suddenly seems like it wasn't enough and you wonder if you are really prepared.

Either way, when you arrive at the hospital, you will have to check in and get monitored to make sure the baby and you are both fine. Feel free to skip this part if you get there and the baby is already on their way out! They monitor the baby's heartbeat and your contractions. They also check how much you are dilated and effaced. This means your doctor checks your cervix, the lower end of the uterus, to find out if it has opened up and thinned out. Once you are dilated and effaced to a certain degree, you get transferred to your room. You will have some time to settle in and change before getting back onto the monitors.

One thing you probably have not realized is now you cannot eat anything before delivery. You can drink water and eat a popsicle, but no hamburger or anything like that! So, make sure you do not arrive there feeling hungry. When you get to your room, you get to know the nurse taking care of you, and you can prepare for labor. Go over the birth plan with your nurse so they know what is really important to you. They will try their best to support you with everything you have in the plan. Just be aware things can change very quickly if there is an emergency that comes up. Or maybe you put on your plan that you want to use a ball during labor, but now you realize this is the last thing you want to try out. Or you get an epidural and can't feel your legs anymore; you will have to lie down instead of bouncing on the ball.

Be open for change when things do not go as planned, and don't be disappointed. The health of your baby and yourself comes above everything else. That also counts for trends you might see on social media like putting lots of makeup on to look pretty when the baby is born. I have nothing against that. Quite the opposite: whatever it is that makes you feel better, and gets you through the pain and work your body will go through, go for it. No one should tell you what to do or not to do when it comes to these little details. All I am saying is you should not let others pressure you into doing anything you aren't comfortable with when you are giving birth, just to please someone else.

You do you, whatever that means for you. You want to put on makeup, great. You want to take a shower, go for it. If you have a doula to get you through this without any pain medication, good for you. You get the epidural right away, good for you. Giving birth is the most powerful thing anyone can do on the planet. YOU decide how YOU do it for YOU.

I want to briefly touch on the topic of pain management during labor. Some women know from the very beginning they want either a natural birth or an epidural. For others, like myself, it was not as clear cut. I would have definitely preferred a natural birth, but knew having labor pains over a long period of time would wear me down. I told myself I would try it as long as I could stand it, and then ask for an epidural. With my first baby, I made it eight hours, just out of pride to not seem weak. I was getting nauseous, started throwing up, and got diarrhea. This was my body's reaction to the immense pain. I asked the doctor how long it could possibly still take, and they told me it could take another eight hours or just one hour, who knows? He brought up an excellent point though: I needed to keep in mind my energy levels. If I didn't want an epidural and went through another eight hours of this pain, I might get so exhausted I wouldn't have the energy to push the baby out at that point. This would lead to a C-section, which I definitely did not want. My husband would have preferred a natural birth without an epidural as well, but seeing me in pain like this, he supported me with whatever I requested. Just not the laughing gas they offered there as well, that was just too weird for the both of us! For me, getting the epidural was the best decision. I could finally get some rest and sleep; the diarrhea disappeared, and I felt energetic and excited when it was time to have the baby. I have the utmost respect for women who give birth without any pain medication. Some women have very good control over their bodies through meditation and can handle the pain very well. Doulas offer an additional way of support and might have some tricks to get you through the contractions more comfortably. Another option you can explore is hypnosis. Take a little bit of time to think about what you feel comfortable with. Having somewhat of a plan can make you feel less nervous and more confident.

One of the questions you will need to prepare for is: are you telling anyone that labor is starting or not? Initially, I thought I would tell my mom for sure, as soon as it starts and keep her posted. Then I talked to my husband about it and we decided against it. Why? First of all, there was a six hour time difference between my mother living in Germany and me having the baby in the United States. If it would happen during night time in her time zone, she would not sleep. Timelines for giving birth are unpredictable, and for some unlucky ones like me, labor can take a very long time. If I had notified my mother about going to the hospital and then not written to her for 24 hours because nothing had happened, she might have gotten really worried. Being one of the lucky ones, her delivery experience was fast, maybe a little too fast. I also knew when the baby was finally born, I wanted to have bonding time with her and figure out how to hold the baby, how to change a diaper, how to feed her, and all these things you really won't know unless you have been around babies, which I had not.

We shared the news with family and friends several hours after the baby was born, giving us the chance to fully concentrate on our daughter and not worry about phone distractions such as answering questions or taking and sending pictures. This is what worked out for us. It does not mean you have to do it the same way. If you want to keep everyone in your family posted during the process, go for it. This is just to show you a different option and make you think about what you might want to do.

Now it's time to finally have your baby! When you give birth, don't be surprised about all the people who will be in your room. There are usually one or two nurses, a midwife, a doctor, maybe a student resident, your partner or a different support person, a doula if you chose one, and a photographer if you hired one. When I was first told about this, I was a little concerned I would feel embarrassed or overwhelmed, but when it came to having the baby, I really didn't care anymore. You are not the first one to have a baby, right??

They have seen it all. And that means ALL. The pain of the contractions is excruciating. I won't sugarcoat that at all. If you decide to go through the pain unmedicated, it can happen that you get nauseous from the pain and have to throw up. You will poop during labor. This is normal and all women do it. You probably won't even know it when you do it, but for the doctors and nurses it's just part of 'business as usual,' so don't worry about it. Labor is messy and not pretty, but it IS beautiful. You can even watch it. They offer mirrors to see what's going on. If you don't want that, but still want to be involved, you can feel the head of the baby when it comes out. Some hospitals even allow the partners to be involved in the delivery and let them catch the baby. Another not so enjoyable part about the delivery is the tearing. Maybe you are one of the few lucky ones who won't tear, but most women do. If you went for the epidural, at least you won't feel it. Whatever you decide, and no matter how much it hurts, try to embrace it. What you are doing is incredible and a miracle. When you are having your baby, I can only tell you: Congratulations, you just did something amazing!

In the movies they always show these cute, pink, chubby, clean, crying babies when they are born. This is not the case. Babies are usually not cute when they are born. They have a weird color, very pale and almost grayish, and can come out with a white creamy substance on them. That is the vernix caseosa, a coating to protect the baby's skin. If they are born vaginally, then they can have a cone head from the birth canal. Not all of them cry right away, and need some intense rubbing to get them going. They might also have mucus in their mouth which needs to be sucked away. Just trust the nurses and doctors who know exactly what they are doing. After a minute, the baby will look much healthier and baby-like, and they will place the baby on top of you. This will be done skin to skin, your naked baby on top of your bare chest. It doesn't matter if you are breastfeeding or formula feeding; it is very beneficial for the baby and the parent as well. If the mother has a C-section, the baby will be placed on the partner for skin-to-skin contact. It is a practice that should be continued after delivery as well. For the baby to spend time with their father skin to skin is almost equally as beneficial as when the mother cuddles with the baby. There are two main differences between the mother having skin to skin time with the baby compared to the father: the milk production improves, and the mother's breasts can regulate the baby's body temperature, either heating the baby up or cooling them down, whereas father's chest only heats up. Besides that, all other benefits for the baby can be achieved by cuddling with the father as well. And who would say no to this precious snuggle time?

When you first hold your baby, be in the moment and enjoy every second of it. After everything you have put your body through, this is your grand prize! You usually get about 1½ to 2 hours after delivery to bond with your baby. A few minutes after the baby is born, the umbilical cord gets cut. Often, the partners like to do this special task, other times it's the mother herself, and some prefer the doctor or nurse to do it for them. After giving birth to your baby, you are not done yet. You will also have to deliver your placenta. One question the doctor will ask you is if you want to see your placenta, or maybe even want to keep it. This is a personal preference. I didn't care about it because I just wanted to look at my baby. I just cared about the fact my baby arrived healthy, and I didn't have to deal with any problematic issues. Even though this is not scientifically proven, some women believe that eating their placenta brings great health benefits like prevention of anemia or increased energy levels. Currently it is not known if eating placenta is safe or not. Should you decide to keep your placenta, you will have to provide for storage and transfer it to whatever service provider will make it into pills for you.

After this, while you are enjoying bonding with your baby, you will also get stitched up if you tear during labor, then get cleaned up. I honestly don't even remember this part because I was so focused on the baby I didn't pay attention to what the doctor was doing. The baby will also get checked for weight and height, temperature and well-being. This only takes a few minutes, then you have your baby back with you. If you have the awareness for it, take some pictures as well. My husband snapped a picture of me holding the baby shortly after birth for both of our daughters, which made those pictures the girls' very first photo shoot! This was a very special momentous moment to me.

During the first two hours of bonding time, you will also attempt to feed the baby for the first time, either breastfeeding or with a bottle. Babies are born with the sucking reflex, so most of the time it works without a problem. With my first baby, I struggled. She drank a little bit herself and then we ended up hand expressing some colostrum drops to give her. Colostrum is the first form of breast milk and yellow, so don't expect white milk to come out of your breasts from the very beginning.

These first two hours together go by quickly. Afterwards, when everything with the baby and yourself is fine, you get transferred to the postpartum area of the hospital where you usually stay in a different room than where you gave birth. Make sure you take everything with you to the new room and don't forget anything.

Welcome to parenthood. In the next chapter we will look at the rest of your hospital stay.

Memory Box

Picture of the Room Where you Gave Birth

Get the Name of the Nurse and Doctor Caring for You

Picture of the Board in the Room with Information of Parents and Baby

First Picture of Your Baby

Any Important Items that Helped you During Labor and Delivery

Take Placenta if you Want to Get it Transformed into Pills

Baby's Hospital Bracelet

_____

_____

_____

_____

_____

_____

Your Hospital Stay

You went through the hardest part of the journey and gave birth to your baby. It is time to recover and learn how to be a parent.

When it was time for me to go to the postpartum area of the hospital, I still couldn't feel my legs completely with both of my deliveries. So, it was time to rest some more, get checked up on by the nurses, and enjoy the baby until I was able to be fully functional again. With my first baby, we stayed at the hospital for two days after the delivery; with the second one, only one day. I was initially shocked how short the stay would be because in Germany, I would have stayed three days. Since I had no clue how to handle a baby, I wanted to stay there longer, rather than shorter, to get all the support possible. In the end, the two days, and even the one day with my second baby were completely sufficient. I was actually looking forward to leaving. Not because I didn't like the care, quite the contrary, the nurses and doctors were amazing. We had all the support we needed, and the food was rather good as well. It was just exhausting to be checked up on constantly, and not getting proper rest in between the feedings of the baby. Sometimes they came in to check on me, just to return thirty minutes later with the next painkiller in the middle of the night. An hour later, a check up on the baby, and so on. The beds were the motorized ones that constantly moved and adjusted their mattress positions to avoid any sore spots. Yes, good for the body, but not very helpful with resting. Besides being tired, I was glad I had the two days with my first baby in the hospital.

As a new parent, there are so many questions that come up that would not enter your mind when you are pregnant. I struggled so much with breastfeeding with my first baby. Luckily, I had taken a breastfeeding class before to be prepared it might not come as naturally as everyone made it seem. My daughter wouldn't latch properly, and when she was finally latched, she didn't always suck well, so sometimes she couldn't get anything to eat. It was very frustrating, but I had the good fortune of being surrounded by very supportive nurses who helped me hand express the colostrum so my daughter was fed properly. My nipples were hurting, and it was overwhelming. After speaking with the onsite lactation consultant, I knew I was doing the right thing and just had to keep practicing until she got it.

My second baby was a natural at breastfeeding. As soon as I tried feeding her, she latched like a magnet and ate in one feeding what felt like as much as my first baby ate in one day! With the second one, everything was easier concerning the handling of the baby because we knew how to hold her, how to change her diapers, and enjoyed these moments with her more than with the first one when we were nervous and insecure. We were much more tired the second time around because of the lack of sleep. Another difference between the first and second one was the amount of support the nurses gave us up front. With our first baby we had to fill out a paper every time she peed or pooped, when she ate and how much (if hand expressed or formula), or how much time she was breastfeeding. We also had to list how much time we spent skin to skin with her. It was helpful to get a feel for what was normal for her. With our second baby they just asked us how it went. If we had asked for more support, we would have gotten it, but we simply didn't need it. Overall, it was great to be in a hospital we really liked and felt cared for.

Now that you are a parent, how do you feel? This is a very emotional moment and for most parents, it's immediate love. But not for all. Some parents don't have this immediate connection with their babies, and question themselves if this means they are bad parents. This is not the case. It is actually quite normal, and happens to more parents than you would think. For some, it takes a little bit of time to establish this bond. Especially for mothers who went through a tough labor, and who are extremely exhausted, physically and mentally. It can be hard to look at the baby and feel the complete opposite of all they have just gone through.

Don't feel bad if this happens to you. Give yourself some space and enjoy the bonding time until that motherly love hits you. You just went through so much; your hormones are out of control and you might be overwhelmed and insecure about what's going on and how to take care of your baby. Be patient with yourself and focus on the care of your baby; everything else will come later. It's ok to not know everything, and to feel weird and out of place. Ask for help where/when you need it. How do you change diapers? How do you swaddle your baby? How do you feed the baby and then burp him/her? How do you hold this tiny human and make sure to not hurt them? How do you pass the baby on to the next person? It is ok to ask the nurses to do it for you so you can watch and learn. Everyone wants the best for their baby, so if you need some time, take it.

Besides taking care of the baby, another huge focus will be to take care of yourself. If you had an epidural, the nurse will help you go to the restroom for the first time and make sure you won't take a fall. If you went through labor with no anesthesia, the nurse will still go with you. I felt awkward that there was someone else going to the restroom with me, but they just need to make sure I was ok. She collected my urine to see if there were any larger blood clots, the size of golf balls or bigger, to make sure there weren't any issues with the bleeding. Then she showed me how to change my net underwear with the pad (reminded me more of a miniature puppy training mat!) and ice pad, and how to clean myself with the squirt bottle afterwards. I was afraid urinating would hurt and burn, but luckily, not much discomfort.

What helps is to stay hydrated. Yes, you have to urinate more often, but the urine won't be as concentrated and, therefore, not hurt as much. After the delivery, I couldn't really feel when I was urinating. Everything was just too stretched out after pushing a baby out, but it does get better every day. It sounds a little crazy, but the first trip to the bathroom is like a little milestone. The next larger milestone is the first time you poop. I was worried about urinating the first time, but afraid of pooping. The nurse will give you a stool softener to make it easier for you. Somehow, I thought it would hurt, but I was lucky on this one. You just have to make sure to clean yourself properly.

Speaking to many women, what surprised me was to find out how many of them were unprepared for the amount of bleeding after giving birth. It is not like you give birth and during the delivery, all the blood comes out and you are good to go. Inside the uterus, it is almost like you have a big wound, which needs to heal and this does not happen from one day to the next. You will still bleed quite a bit. This bleeding is called lochia, and it is a mix of mucous, tissue and blood. The first few days are the worst, but in less than a week, it usually subsides considerably. When you breastfeed, your body releases the hormone oxytocin. It makes your uterus contract which is painful, causing you to bleed more. The bleeding after giving birth can last up to six weeks. Towards the end it becomes very little, but it will last much longer than your period. Initially, it is lots of blood, so make sure to buy the biggest sanitary napkins you can find. Tampons are a no-go in this situation. First of all, you need to heal. It even sounds very painful to attempt using tampons. More importantly, they pose a risk of infection.

During your hospital stay, the nurses will check your uterus every couple hours after delivery, then less frequently the day after. You lay down on your back and they press really hard on your lower belly to feel the shrinking of your uterus. This is painful but part of the recovery process. The painkillers definitely help.

You will still have a belly after having your baby, and it will take a little time to get rid of it. I remember my belly feeling just wobbly and mushy. The abdominal muscles get so stretched out they really don't help out at all after delivery. I still looked six months pregnant when I left the hospital. Just another aspect of motherhood to embrace! Luckily, this changes with time. Don't feel discouraged. You just had a baby. Cut yourself some slack.

The biggest change and adjustment for new parents usually is the lack of sleep. During those first nights, it can be very helpful for your partner to get up as well to support with the feedings. My husband would get up with me and change our daughter's diaper while I went to the restroom to change my pad. Then I went to the always moving hospital bed and had him carry her over so I could feed her. If I felt too weak, or in too much pain to scoot over to the side of the bed and get up to carry her to the bassinet, I called him to pick her up. With my first baby, I really felt those stitches the first days when getting up from the bed or sitting down, so I preferred for him to help more. With our second baby, I recovered much faster, and I had less pain, so I wouldn't call him anymore and let him rest. It was enough for me to be exhausted.

This way, he could take care of her during the day while I took a nap. The baby needs to eat every two to three hours initially and does not care if you are tired and want to sleep. If you are formula feeding, it is possible to take turns feeding to get more rest. But even then, you initially don't get your full night's sleep. Luckily, babies are tired right after being born and usually sleep well the first day, so you also get the chance to nap while they are sleeping. Try to get as much rest as possible.

That brings up another point. Do you want to have visitors while you are in the hospital? How about a welcome home 'surprise' get-together? Of course, everyone is really excited when there is a new addition to the family. Grandparents usually can't wait to meet the newest grandchild. And the rest of the family. And the friends. You probably want to show off your baby. Before you invite everyone over and come up with a schedule of who can be at the hospital during visiting hours, just see how you feel after giving birth. Recovery can be rough. You might not feel like taking a shower right away and you might prefer to sleep or just cuddle with the baby, or just figure out how to change diapers and how to feed the baby, instead of entertaining visitors.

We didn't want to have any visitors when we had our first daughter, and made that clear to everyone. It didn't matter if they were offended, this was not about pleasing them, it was about us as a family. With our second baby, it wasn't even an option due to the pandemic. Not even our older daughter was allowed into the hospital and had to stay with our friends. I would have probably

been fine with my mother coming over, but she was in Germany, so that was that! If you think about all these factors and still want to have visitors, then please indulge, show off your baby, and have them pamper you while they are there. Maybe they can bring your favorite food or something you miss.

Eventually, yet very quickly, the hospital stay will come to an end. Do you feel ready to go home? You probably have established a routine in the hospital and feel more confident there. Use this time to ask some final questions you might have. This is the first time you will leave the floor of the hospital with your baby and you might feel like they should have quizzed you before leaving to make sure you know what you are doing. Fact is: you WILL be fine! You can go home where you feel most comfortable, where you will have just about everything you need and are familiar with.

Before you can actually leave, there will be some paperwork you need to complete. All the medical records for you and the baby, release forms, and you also need to fill out the paperwork to request the Social Security Number and birth certificate. The nurses will want to watch you buckle your baby into the car seat and double check the baby is safe before you get released.

You are on your way home, ready to introduce your baby to the world. Let's see what the next few weeks will look like.

Memory Box

Picture of the Room Where you Spent the First Few Days Together

Get the Name of the Nurse and Doctor Caring for You

Picture of the Board in the Room with Information of Parents and Baby

Hat for the Baby

Wristbands for you, the Baby, and Your Partner

Foot Print if They Offer it

Newspaper of the Day the Baby was Born

First Outfit Your Baby Wore

_____

_____

_____

_____

_____

Baby's First Six Weeks

You gave birth to your baby and learned the basics of baby care in the hospital. You requested your baby's Social Security Number and birth certificate. You left the hospital and realized this is all on you. Oops… No more help from the nurses and doctors. Now what?

When we drove home with our first daughter after leaving the hospital, it felt surreal. It was a fifteen-minute drive, and I was just hoping no one would hit our car while listening to the baby's breath to make sure she was ok in the car seat. When we arrived home, we were very curious to see how our two cats would react, a very cute British shorthair couple. The Tomcat is very needy and cuddly and wants attention all the time. He loves feeling the touch of humans, so he will always lie down somewhere where he can make sure at least one paw is touching one of us. Of course, we were worried he would lie on top of our daughter and suffocate her, so we never left her unsupervised when he was around.

When the cats finally met her, they sniffed her and left, uninterested, almost scared of her and the unfamiliar smell, not sure what to make of her. That was a pleasant surprise. That evening, our neighbor brought over a homemade dish and it was the best food we could have asked for. She dropped off the dish in front of the door and texted us it was ready to get picked up from the porch; we just had to put it in the oven and enjoy. She didn't even want to bother talking to us so we could focus on the baby and rest. That was the sweetest and most perfect thing she could have done for us and a gesture we now replicate with family and friends having babies.

After dinner, we moved to check how much of our initial planning of the room setup still felt right. We decided our baby would sleep in our room in a bassinet for two weeks, then we would move her to her crib in her own room. Doors closed, of course, so the cats wouldn't be able to get in and try to cuddle in her crib with her. In our room we set up a temporary diaper station on the floor with some puppy training mats to avoid any messes on the carpet. Next to it I had a chair to feed her and the lamp was outfitted with a special night bulb, very helpful to avoid fully waking up at night. During the first night, we realized the setup didn't work as imagined and reorganized things in the middle of the night and everything worked more smoothly.

Like any new parents, we were terrified of SIDS, sudden infant death syndrome, so with every noise the baby made we woke up, listening to her breathing to make sure she was ok. She was a great sleeper and we had to wake her up for the feedings every two to three hours, following the doctor's recommendations. The feedings were not so easy initially, causing some self-doubt. But we made it through the first night at home, and all the following ones as well. After about four days, my milk came in, which was very uncomfortable and painful, and it took a few days to regulate itself to a normal level. On top of that, my hormones were going crazy. When the baby cried and I didn't know what was going on or how to console her, I sat on the couch and cried. That was on day five and it was overwhelming. The most wanted baby will make you frustrated, angry, and upset. That is ok, it's part of the process and you will get through it. That is when I learned I had to take it one day at a time, and not feel like I had to be this perfect mother who knew her child inside out.

With our second daughter, I anticipated things were not going to be smooth. She ate like a champ, which took away one worry, but the big unknown this time around was the sibling factor. How would our older daughter react to her new sister? She was less than two years old when we brought home the baby and the first day she met her, she was nice to her but didn't really know what to do with her. Our older daughter loved body contact and cuddling, and enjoyed being carried. After the delivery, I was not able to carry her anymore, and that's when she had her jealous moment and she cried. She didn't understand why I could carry the baby, but not her. Luckily, this only lasted one morning. Afterwards, she was the sweetest older sister one could imagine. She took such good care of her and every morning she couldn't wait to see her. I made sure to sit down on the floor and have my older daughter sit on my lap, constantly cuddling with her to give her the attention she was craving. Crisis averted!

Bringing your baby home from the hospital is a huge step. Things are very different at home. You developed a routine in the hospital and now everything is changing again. Give yourself some time to figure out what works for you and what doesn't. You probably have preconceived ideas of how you want to do things, how everything should be set up, and how perfect everything will be. Commercials on TV, in magazines, and on social media, always portray the perfect happy family. Baby is either sleeping or super relaxed and happy; the parents look like they've had the best night's sleep and a nice long shower! This is really not reality. Of course, you will have your picture-perfect moments, but you will also struggle to figure out what is going on with your baby and question if this was really a good idea. These tough moments feel extremely frustrating, but they pass and then you see the sleeping little angel and realize they don't do these things on purpose to drive you insane, they are simply trying to figure out the world around them. Don't feel like your baby needs to fit your perfect ideas. Change what doesn't work and adjust to the baby. Trying to mold your baby into a romanticized situation will not work, so save the frustration on both sides and take it as it comes.

One very important decision to make is the sleeping arrangement for your baby. Do you want to have the baby in your room or not? If so, for how long? For some women, co-sleeping is an attractive option because it gets rid of the hassle of getting up in the middle of the night to feed the baby. The ability to quickly attend to a crying baby makes it convenient. For some parents, the close contact with the baby is rewarding and they believe it helps their babies and parents feel safer. Despite the supposed benefits, co-sleeping is generally not recommended as it poses a safety risk for the baby. It increases the risk of SIDS, or so-called sleeping accidents, like rolling on top of your baby in your sleep. It is recommended to have the baby sleep in the same room with you for the first year for the same reason: it decreases the risk of SIDS. At the same time, babies don't sleep as well, which makes the parents not sleep as well. In the end, you have to decide what is the best for you and your family. What worked best for us was to have our babies sleep in their own room after two weeks. Babies make many weird, but perfectly normal noises when they sleep, so we didn't sleep well with them in our room. My husband and I are both light sleepers, which made the decision that much easier. Therefore, the best choice was to get them out of our room. We all slept so much better, and we had ears and eyes on them with a baby monitor. We eventually did turn down the sound level to where we did not have to hear every single sound. If the best choice for you is to have your baby there with you, then go for it. Don't compare yourself to others, because what works for some, will not necessarily work for you. It is always good to know the options, all have their pros and cons, but decide based on what works for you and your family. Trying to force something that does not feel natural will probably end in frustration.

The recovery for the mother continues, while at the same time you are figuring out your baby at home. Breastfeeding still causes you cramps, but it helps with your recovery and should go away after a week or two. After the first week, the bleeding should also be much less and more manageable. Continue to take good care of yourself, per your doctor's guidance and change the pads regularly to avoid any infections. Take painkillers as needed, those stitches need to heal properly. Some women like to use the witch-hazel pads to help with the pain and healing of the tearing. I found it uncomfortable and stopped using it after the second day at home. Another healing remedy helpful to some are the sitz baths. Some women like to use it to help with the healing process. Others don't want to sit in dirty water while they are bleeding. Find out what you are most comfortable with and what makes you feel better.

If you are breastfeeding, the milk comes in shortly after you leave the hospital, about five days after giving birth. So far, your baby had colostrum, now it changes to white milk. You will for sure know when your milk comes in because you wake up with rock-hard breasts that look two sizes bigger than before! It is a little bit painful, and it takes some time to self-regulate. Let the baby eat whenever they want, and if it is too painful in between feedings, you can pump a little bit. However, only pump until you have relief, though, or else you will start producing much more milk than you need. One thing to look out for when breastfeeding is Mastitis. It is an infection of breast tissue that can be caused by a blocked milk duct or bacteria. A blocked milk duct happens if the breast is not fully drained during feedings. If this happens, try to feed more often and let the baby fully drain one breast before offering the other one. You can also pump to drain your breast completely. If Mastitis is caused by bacteria, it can be treated with antibiotics. Those antibiotics do not harm the baby and you can continue breastfeeding.

Another challenge is the cluster feeding. It also happens in bottle-fed babies, but not as intensely as in breastfed babies. Cluster feeding happens between three to six weeks of age, but also whenever there is a growth spurt. Bottle-fed babies might just want to eat a bigger portion while staying on their schedule, or might want to eat more frequently. With breastfed babies, cluster feeding is a way for the baby to order more milk. The mother's milk supply works as demand and supply. The more the baby wants to eat, the more milk will be produced. When bottle feeding a baby, you have a very good understanding of how much milk the baby actually drinks. You see how many ounces are consumed in each feeding. When breastfeeding, you really have no idea unless you pump and feed the milk from a bottle.

When you don't know how much your baby is eating and they are cluster feeding, it can be very stressful to feel like you are not producing enough milk, worrying that your baby might still be hungry and won't get the nutrition they need. This self-doubt is normal and happens even with the second or third baby. If you have had no issues feeding your baby enough milk, then most likely you are still satisfying your baby, they just eat more frequently. For me, it was alarming I was feeding so often with both my daughters and my breasts always felt empty, yet they seemed to always want to drink more. But after a couple of days, the milk supply went up, and they were completely content. My nurse told me you can never really run empty. Your body will always respond to the baby's needs so it will keep producing. The biggest learning curve for me was to not plan anything for those days, I knew I would spend almost half the day on the couch feeding the baby, so I made sure I had a water bottle and a granola bar with me at all times. The more relaxed you are, the easier it will be. It's ok if nothing else gets done these days. The laundry will still be there the next day, and the dishes can get washed another time. It is ok to ask for help and ask your partner to support you.

If for some reason your body cannot produce enough milk, then you always have the option to supplement with formula. Make sure to offer your breast so the milk supply increases always first over time and feed the rest with formula.

With the tough combination of sleep deprivation, recovery, not knowing what your baby wants sometimes, exhaustion, and that topped with hormones going crazy, it can all seem very overwhelming at times. You might even end up crying, questioning what you are doing, and if this is too much for you. This is just another part of being a parent and even has a name: the Baby Blues. It affects up to 60% - 80% of all new mothers. It happens around three days after delivery and can last for a week or two, and goes away on its own. I was lucky, and I only had it for a few days. Knowing about it and being aware of it helped me out. I was able to tell my husband what was going on so he could support me. It is very important for your partner to keep an eye on you for signs of Baby Blues. Try to be more understanding during this time. It doesn't have to make sense for you. Just try your best to be as supportive as you can. Going through all this is a lot. I once heard these analogies that resonated with the physical demands of this experience- "Giving birth is like being in a car accident, and breastfeeding is like running a marathon every day!" If you, as the partner, are tired and exhausted, then please keep in mind the mother is not only feeling the same exhaustion, but on top of that is still recovering, in pain, and has zero control over her hormones. This is not meant as an excuse, this is just for you to be aware of what might drive moodiness and irritability. Please don't take it personally and talk about it another time. Starting a fight does not help anyone in this situation and might make the blues even worse.

If the Baby Blues lasts longer than two weeks, or the mother has thoughts of harming herself or the baby, or feels like she cannot properly take care of the baby, then seek help from your healthcare provider. This can be a sign of postpartum depression. This is nothing to feel embarrassed about, and you should not feel reluctant to admit it. It is helpful if the partner supports this and starts the conversation when they see signs of depression. The sooner you get help, the faster you will overcome this, and will start enjoying your baby again.

My advice during this rocky period: be as relaxed as possible and prioritize your health. If you have questions or need help, it is as easy as asking for it. If you have the opportunity to have a midwife or social worker come to your house to clarify any questions you might have, take advantage of this opportunity. Their job is to help you out. They want you to succeed as parents, and for your children to grow up in the healthiest situation possible. Ask family and friends for help. If you don't reach out and continue to project the 'picture perfect' family, then they will assume everything is fine. If you ask someone who cares about you to help out with cooking a meal or with laundry, they will usually happily come over and do the task, feeling good about being able to support and help you. Do not feel pressured to host people to meet the baby right away, having to clean and entertain. Take your time and do things at your own pace. Learn to be selfish and say no. Think about what is best for you and your family, not what makes other people around you happy. Establishing that special bond with your baby takes time and effort. Find the routine first before putting more unnecessary stress and work on yourself. When you are physically ready, get out and get some fresh air. Once you feel like you have a handle on things, there is still enough time to show off your precious baby. Have some fun as well and do a newborn photoshoot – either do it yourself or have someone take the pictures for you. Take your first family pictures all together. I think both of my daughters looked much cuter after their first week, to be completely honest.

Most importantly for the new parents: support each other and accept each other. Do not criticize everything the partner is doing and be fine with doing things differently. No-one is perfect, and as long as the baby is taken care of, it is ok to approach things differently. Often the mothers feel like they know better, but that is not actually always the case. Let the partners step up. They want to be involved, and it is a common frustration for them. It is hard for them to find a way to fit in when the moms always seem to 'know best' and push them away. I have never given either of my daughters a bath myself. I have always been there and watched, but this is my husband's thing and he is proud of that. If you pump, let the partner feed the bottle, let them play with the baby. Go get some rest, your body needs it. They can always come and wake you up if they feel like something is wrong with the baby or they need some help.

At the end of the first six weeks, you should feel much better and feel like you know your baby. You probably have a routine established and the initial insecurities are overcome. For the mothers, a big milestone is the six weeks follow up appointment with their doctor. They check if everything is ok and usually clear you to start light exercise and for intimacy with your partner.

Your maternity leave might be over now and soon it will be time to get ready to go back to work. If this is the case, you need to secure childcare. You will need to figure out what the best option for you is: daycare center, academy, in-home daycare, nanny, shared nanny, au pair, family. Again, all come with pros and cons, so make time to discuss this with your partner. Make sure to take a tour of any daycare options outside of your house to make the right decision for your family. At a minimum, you will need to fill out registration paperwork and need a physical exam done by a doctor. You will have to provide extra clothes, bibs, formula or breast milk, diapers, wipes, and whatever else they tell you to bring. Start the process early enough to not run out of time in the end. Choose the option that you feel most comfortable with. With so many options, it can feel overwhelming at times. Trust your instincts! The best match is one that fits your situation, coupled with the place you feel most comfortable and trusting of, and most important, feeling good about the people who will be taking care of your baby.

The initial shock of being a new parent is over and you feel more secure with how to handle your baby and are more in tune with your baby's needs. Now it is time to enjoy the rest of the first year and watch your baby as they grow up.

Memory Box

Footprint of the Baby (You Can Try Handprint, But This One is Tough)

Keep Some of the First Clothes You Like

Take Pictures of Many of the Firsts (First Bath, First Nap in Bassinet, etc.)

Request a Presidential Greeting from the White House

Request a Papal Greeting from the Pope

Take a Picture Every Month for a Collage to Show the First Year

First Family Portrait

Collectibles of Baby's Birth Year (Silver Coin of the Year, Liquor Bottle, Something Fun, Tasty You Can Pass on as a Gift When They Are Older)

_____

_____

_____

Baby's First Year

You survived the first six weeks together as a family and were cleared by the doctor to start doing some light exercises and to be intimate with your partner again. You probably have a routine established and your baby is a little bit more predictable. You feel better about yourself and look forward to the next few months as your baby grows by leaps and bounds.

With our first baby, we planned for me to stay home and not work. We built this into our budget and savings, as I would have done the same in Germany; although there, maternity leave is paid up to the first year. However, this does not mean I had an easy 'year off!' Raising a baby is a 24/7 job, not forty hours a week, like a normal job. Sometimes stay-at-home parents are viewed negatively in society, where economic productivity is a large measure of how one is perceived. Truth be told, going to work is WAY easier than raising a baby and, sadly, not always appreciated as such.

It was the little things that frustrated me. Sometimes I was jealous of my husband, who, at work, could go to the restroom whenever he wanted/needed to, without having to bring along a baby who otherwise would scream or cry from separation anxiety. Or simply yearning for normal, adult conversations without a potential interruption every few minutes. I easily got over the frustration, knowing I was mindful and grateful for the precious time with my constantly-growing daughter. This is time I will never get back and

I know other parents would love the opportunity to spend this time with their children. Working around the baby's sleep schedule became the new normal. I did the shopping, cooking, cleaning; took my daughter to doctor's appointments and other chores to make sure we had quality family time in the evenings and on the weekends when we were all together. It was an amazing experience to have all this time with her, even with all of the ups and downs.

When she was ten months old, I unexpectedly jumped on a once-in-a-lifetime opportunity to help the fight against the COVID-19 pandemic. I started a new job and we took her to a neighboring in-home daycare. I felt like a horrible mother and cried the Friday before she started. My husband took the following week off to help her ease with the transition and finding a new rhythm. He took her to daycare in the morning and she did great with the drop off. I focused on work and the day passed very quickly. I got to pick her up in the afternoon and she had a fun time at daycare. I knew she was well taken care of, and babies don't understand the concept of time yet, so she didn't realize she had not seen me the whole day.

With our second child, I was working during my pregnancy and I took my entire Maternity Leave before going back to work. I couldn't bring myself to take her to daycare full time. I was just not ready for that after only 3½ months. We still didn't have the feeding routine established that I would have expected. This child was more unpredictable. I had a very supportive manager who agreed with me going back to work part time rather than full time. She made it possible for me to stay home with my baby and found a project for me that was 100% remote with flexible part-time hours so I could work when the baby slept. Without this support, I would have had to quit my job. I am very grateful to have been given this opportunity and I plan to continue advocating for other moms throughout my career. I didn't always work the full twenty hours, but I finished all my work and could catch up in the evening after both girls were in bed if I had to. Was it easy? No, especially if it was a rough night when the baby was teething, but then I just pushed through it. We got a cleaning service to help, and planned several days ahead with food so I could go shopping less, but with some planning and discipline, we made it work out.

A big difference between my recoveries after having my daughters was my weight loss. With my first baby, I lost most of my weight after three weeks. I only had one pound to lose and was able to fit into my old clothes without working out or adjusting my diet. Good genes, thank you Mom! With my second child, I finally went to buy new pants after three months because I was just not losing weight. I still needed to lose ten pounds after six months, but no matter what I did, nothing helped. I kept telling myself that maybe once I stop breastfeeding, I will go back to my old self.

That being said, please don't worry about the "did you lose the weight yet?" questions. Now that you are cleared to work out again, go ahead and do some light exercises if you feel up to it. If you would rather take a nap, give that priority. You need all the rest you can get while you are still getting up at night. Everyone loses their weight differently, just like every pregnancy is different. Pay attention to your diet and make healthy choices. It is totally ok to give into your cravings as well, though. I love chocolate, and if I crave some, I will eat some. Not in exaggerated portions, but in moderation, a piece here and there. Try to move around. I did not get a diaper changing station on the main level where we spent most of our time, forcing myself to walk up the stairs to the nursery whenever I needed to change diapers. Just that one flight of stairs made me feel better, like it was a mini workout, and those were the mini victories to look out for. At the end of the day, it's the small victories that make a difference. It can be quite frustrating to see other moms thin and fit shortly after giving birth when you yourself are struggling to lose the weight. If you have a hard time motivating yourself to work out, see if there is a stroller walking group where you live, or a new mom workout class to join a group of other mothers who are going through the same issues. Sometimes having others cheering you on and holding you accountable gives you just the kick you need! It is also a good setting to make new friends for playdates.

No matter if you are back to your old self or not, the six weeks clearance is a milestone to look forward to. Now that you are healed and cleared, your partner might expect you can have sex just like you used to. While it might be a milestone your partner is eagerly looking forward to, it might not be the same for you. If you both are looking forward to it, then have fun. If you don't feel ready for it yet, then take your time and don't rush. Being physically ready and mentally ready are two very different things. If you had a rough day with your baby, are sleep deprived, and your hormones are getting the better of you, then maybe it's not the best day to give it a try. This can create conflict with your partner, so be open and talk about it. I was quite nervous before the first time because I didn't know if it would be painful or not, but it is something you won't find out unless you try. When you are breastfeeding, your estrogen levels decline dramatically, leading to vaginal dryness. This is why it is recommended to use a lubricant when having intercourse again. In general, just do whatever you feel comfortable with. Try to enjoy these intimate opportunities. Most of your time is used up by taking care of your baby, but it is just as important to make sure you stay connected to your partner and focus on each other as well. The easiest time is when the baby is sleeping, not to get interrupted easily. Discuss birth control. Some people think breastfeeding is a safe method of contraception, but it is NOT. Women can get pregnant while breastfeeding. My doctor told me to wait eighteen to twenty-four months between pregnancies to reduce the risk of health issues and pregnancy complications. We waited twelve months, and I felt ready for the next pregnancy, at least from a physical aspect.

Just like the first six weeks, the rest of the time with your baby until they turn one year old will be filled with good days and bad days. Just because you made it through the first six weeks doesn't mean you suddenly know everything. It is ok to still be unsure about some things and to ask for help and input. I have found it very helpful to have friends with children of the same age and exchange ideas of who does what and how. You don't have to do things the way others are doing them, but it is extremely helpful to be aware of other options, especially if you run out of your own! Continue doing your own thing and stay true to your values. Do not give up on what's important to you because it is not convenient or others find it too much or too different. Do not compare yourself to others, especially when it comes to the development of your baby. Every baby is different and hits milestones at their own pace. You might see other families and think they have everything under control: perfect baby, perfect parents. Trust me, this is just a snapshot you see, not what is going on behind closed doors. Everyone struggles with something. Yes, their baby might sleep through the night when yours is not, but perhaps your baby eats solids earlier than theirs. It is not a competition or a race. What matters is that your baby is loved and well taken care of. Learn to trust your instincts.

Everyone else around you also seems to know better and will give you unsolicited advice on how to do things and what you are doing wrong. This will probably not stop until your children are old enough to move out and live their own lives. It is very annoying and frustrating, especially on days you are struggling to keep your baby happy. Try to keep in mind these people mean well and want the best for you and your baby. Reminding myself of this made it easier for me to deal with them. If the advice gets to be too intrusive, set your boundaries, thank them, let them know you appreciate their input, but you are the parent and know your child best, so no advice is necessary.

The worst case of this I experienced was in Peru. We took our first daughter there when she was four months old. Although it was the rainy season, we only experienced two days of rain, and the weather was great. All the Peruvian women loved our daughter and immediately indicated that our daughter was cold and we needed to dress her appropriately! This was not only once in a while, but sometimes every five minutes. On one of our day trips, we had to tell not only the tour guide, but the entire group we traveled with to please keep their concerns to themselves and let us enjoy our trip because we were the parents and knew what was best for our baby. We let them know she was not cold, could happily sleep on the seat in the bus, and after this we finally enjoyed the rest of the day after a few apologies along the way.

You will also get advice from older generations about how things were done 'back in the day.' Fact is that what was done thirty or forty years ago is not necessarily the recommendation anymore. It can be difficult when your own parents are trying to tell you what you need to do and you disagree with them, but you need to stand your ground and do what is right for you, not for them. Be selfish, do what's best for you and your family. Your baby has a routine and it is best for you to follow it so your baby won't be fussy and crying the rest of the day, and possibly the next day. Often it is not worth breaking this routine. It is easier for others around you to meet your schedule than your entire family trying to meet theirs.

The first year with your baby is probably one of the most important ones and a beautiful one. There are so many milestones to celebrate and look forward to, but you should not forget to celebrate yourself as well. The easiest way to do this is to find supportive friends who are truly happy for you and motivate you, and who are there for you when you are frustrated and need to vent without judging you. I have found the most understanding and supportive friends are those who are parents themselves and really know what you are going through because they have experienced the same.

The pinnacle of the first year with your baby is, of course, their first birthday. Congratulations to your baby and congratulations to you, you made it! Celebrate this big event and do it in your style, however you feel is appropriate for you and your baby. This was most likely the best year of your life, and at the same time the most frustrating and challenging one as well. There is nothing that makes you happier than seeing your baby laugh and be happy. You are now a very experienced parent, but still have no idea what lies ahead of you. Are you ready for the next one?

There are still many milestones and topics I did not go into detail about because they are too important and broad to only mention briefly. The next chapters will cover some of them more in depth.

Memory Box

Take Pictures of Many of the Firsts (First Solids, First Crawl, and so on)

Take a Picture Every Month for a Collage to Show the First Year

Cut the First Lock of Hair for Safe-keeping

Books/Magazines of the Year in Review

Establish a Memory Box You Can Keep Working on Over the Years

Get an Album That Covers the First Year with Milestones and Pictures

Something from First Mother's Day and Father's Day

_____

_____

_____

_____

_____

Eating Habits

We just finished a broad overview of the first year of your baby, concluding with the grand finale: their first birthday. Now we can look at some of the important topics a bit more in depth. We will start off with a more detailed view on one of the most important concerns: eating. This includes breastfeeding, some bottle feeding, and solids.

When I was pregnant with our first baby, it was clear to me I would be breastfeeding. There was no doubt in my mind I would not have any issues and could provide for my baby without a problem. Then I met some expectant mothers who were not so sure if they could produce any milk or enough milk, so I started thinking about possible difficulties I could encounter myself. I received my care in the military facility, Fort Belvoir Community Hospital, and they offered classes to expectant parents, commonly referred to as "centering." This was a group setting in which eight to ten pregnant women, expecting their babies all in the same month, took the classes together and had their check-ups right before the classes. I really enjoyed this setting as it gave me the opportunity to make friends who would have babies the same age. Additionally, the women's clinic in the hospital offered extra classes for everyone who was not able to join the group sessions. This included a class on breastfeeding and the nurses encouraged the partners to join, listen, and learn.

We signed up at the last minute and unexpectedly, my husband got called on duty, so I went on my own. This class was one of the best classes I attended and left me feeling very prepared. I knew then that breastfeeding does not necessarily happen without problems, and could take up to six weeks to establish a good routine with your baby. I felt good knowing I had access to lactation consultants in case I needed them. I liked the class so much I signed up again so my husband could hear all this as well. This made a big difference for both of us to know what to expect, and also to find out how he could be supportive during the feeding and help out. When I had our first daughter, sure enough, she had trouble latching on properly. I had enough colostrum to feed her sufficiently; it was just difficult to get her to the point to drink properly. During my hospital stay I had six different nurses help me hand express colostrum to feed the drops to my baby to make sure she ate enough. We had the support we needed to figure out a somewhat decent latch so she could drink on her own by the time we went home. I still struggled for a couple weeks to feel like it was natural. I called her "My Toothless Vampire" because even without a single tooth, she bit so hard, I had a wound on my nipple! I tried using a nipple shield to protect the wounded area, but she had a hard time latching on to it. I tried every single position with her we could come up with to find a good way for her to latch. It was very frustrating, difficult, and painful, but eventually we made it through the hard part and after about four weeks we knew how to feed. From then on there was no stopping her!

With our second daughter, it was the complete opposite. I mentally prepared myself to go through the same struggles again, knowing how tough it could be. When I tried feeding her the first time, it was like two matching puzzle pieces. No issues at all. She latched on without a problem and ate a huge portion, at least compared to my first one. She was a great eater. Her nickname was "My Magnet." Sometimes I hadn't even positioned her properly in my arms and she was already latched on, eating away. Considering our values, lifestyle, and current medical guidance, for us it was also the most convenient option as we love traveling. No matter when and where we were, the food was always readily available for our baby.

When thinking about how to feed their baby, most women will consider breastfeeding. It is recommended to breastfeed your baby for the first two years, per the World Health Organization (WHO). The first six months should exclusively be breast milk. There is a good reason for this. Breast milk is the natural way of giving your baby all the nutrients they need to grow up and develop properly. It is amazing to think your body knows exactly what the perfect composition of your milk is for your baby, and how it needs to change over time to meet the baby's growing needs. It starts after giving birth with feeding them the colostrum, which is the first form of breast milk. It is yellowish and thicker than the white milk that comes in later. Colostrum production starts during your pregnancy between sixteen to twenty-two weeks. It is nutrient rich and helps build up the immune system of the baby. Initially, your baby only needs a small portion to get filled up, but the amount increases over time as the baby's stomach grows. Even if you decide to feed your baby formula, you will still produce colostrum and could consider expressing some of it to give your baby that immunity booster for the first few days. Hospitals have special fridges for storing colostrum to support this important stage.

After two to five days, the more mature milk comes in. It looks white and is not as thick. Milk 'coming in' means the change in composition and the increase in volume. Don't be surprised if you wake up with rock solid, hurting breasts. You will definitely know when your milk comes in. It is very relieving when the baby eats and gets some of that stored-up milk out. Your body needs to adjust to the volume it needs to produce. Milk production follows the demand and supply method. The more milk your baby wants to eat and 'requests,' the more milk your body will produce. It can take up to three weeks after the birth for your body to get used to the normal amount it needs to produce. Until then, it can vary between too much milk and what feels like not enough. Once your body is producing milk properly, you can consider pumping and storing away some extra milk. This can help in emergencies, like having to take antibiotics or other medication that is not recommended during breastfeeding, or having to do surgery. One of the most common fears of a breastfeeding mother is to not produce enough milk for the baby, so they will be hungry and not grow and gain weight properly. My nurses told me it is not possible for the body to "run dry" and not have any milk left. The body will always have some milk produced as it is being consumed, so your baby will not starve. This can be hard to believe when you feel completely drained and your baby is still crying for more milk, so just keep offering them the breast until they are full. Usually, your body increases milk production and your baby gets what they need. In some cases, your body really doesn't produce enough milk and then it is important to realize and acknowledge your baby needs to eat more than you can produce. This is when you might need to supplement with formula, but ensure you remain in contact with your lactation specialist for any questions or concerns.

The decision to start feeding your newborn with formula is most likely because you have to and, in some cases, because you want to. Unfortunately, some of the breastfeeding moms judge the formula feeding parents even though this is none of their business. Formula has been developed to be as close as possible to breast milk, and children who were raised with formula grow up healthy. The biggest decision to make is which one to use. There are different brands, and for each brand there are many different choices depending on issues like baby creating gas, spit-up, or sensitive tummies. When I signed up for baby registries, I started receiving samples from different brands, which is a good way to have an initial supply to test what your baby can handle. If you only formula-feed your baby from birth, the hospital will usually provide formula for the beginning. Make sure to take note of which one works best because if your baby can handle it well, and gets used to it in the hospital, it might be the easiest to continue with this specific brand when you go home.

The nice thing about bottle feeding is that both parents can get equally involved and take turns. Either alternate the feeding or consider doing one night with one parent, the next night the other. This way, at least one of both parents is always well rested. There are recommendations on how much a baby should eat per feeding at a certain age and with a bottle making it easy to have control over that amount. That being said, babies don't necessarily eat the same amount all the time. When bottle-fed babies start cluster feeding, they might want to eat a bigger portion than usual, or they want to eat after a shorter time. Other days, they might not want to finish the entire bottle. If overall, they eat the same amount, it is not a problem for them to adjust the amount between the feedings. Another challenge is to find the right bottle your baby will accept. It can take trying several different bottle styles until you find the one your baby will drink from with the least air intake. During your pregnancy, you can collect five or six different brands of bottles from samples. From there on, it is trial and error!

No matter if you breastfeed or bottle-feed your baby, there will be struggles. Either way, your baby has to figure out how to eat. It might take longer for breastfeeding babies to get the perfect latch but therefore, when bottle feeding, the baby usually swallows more air and needs to get burped more often, even during the feeding. All babies spit up some of the milk and make a mess. With both my babies I didn't use the burp cloths for burping them, but I tucked them underneath the baby's head because both were messy eaters, and there was milk on my clothes otherwise.

Over time, babies will eat less frequently and increase their portions. They should be fed on demand, meaning you feed them when they request it, showing signs of being hungry. Formula-fed babies will eat less often than breast-fed babies after some time. The feeding schedule changes again when you introduce solids.

Solids are introduced around six months of age. Some babies show interest in food earlier and it is ok to start earlier, but not before four months of age. The main point to consider is when you start feeding solids, your baby will still get most of the nutrients they need from breast milk or formula. Some babies are very excited to start eating solids and enjoy trying new flavors, as my second daughter did, and other babies seem to not really care while waiting a little longer as my first daughter did. Introducing solids is a big milestone for parents and very exciting, so it can be disappointing if the baby starts gagging and is finished after one or two spoonful's. Try to keep in mind all your baby is used to is their milk which is easy to swallow and a familiar taste.

Introducing solids changes two variables. It changes the consistency, and it changes the taste. Babies have to learn how to swallow a puree that is not as runny as milk, and they might be surprised by all the new different tastes. As they learn how to swallow properly, they might push the food out of their mouth and make squeamish faces-not because they don't like the food, but they don't know how to handle it. Give them some time and they will get the hang of it. If they have a hard time swallowing initially, you can water down the food with breastmilk or formula to make the transition easier. If your baby doesn't like a certain food immediately, offer it again until they eat it. It can take up to fifteen times for a baby to try a certain food until they like it. Once babies start eating solids, it feels like the messes get bigger, too! I spent more time cleaning than before, but that's part of it. Their hands are very fast and can suddenly aim very well! The food gets on their face, their hair, sometimes their ears, on their clothes, on the floor and, if you are unlucky, also on the wall! My older daughter had such a great time eating with a spoon herself, the tomato rice covered the entire area, including two walls, and by the way, wall erasers become an essential cleaning tool!

When it comes to introducing solids, there are different philosophies. One option is to buy the glasses which show exactly what age group they are for. Initially, they will be very fine purees and get chunky over time until your child can eat real table food. A second option is baby led weaning, where you offer your baby finger foods from the very beginning. You start with soft foods and supervise as they feed themselves so they don't bite off chunks too big. With this option, you skip purees altogether. A third option is to go your own route in between. You make your own food for the baby and adjust the consistency and style depending on your baby's interest. This is the route we chose, and it worked well for us. We love cooking and baking, and put great value on overall healthy food of good quality. I started off with cooking my own baby food as purees, getting ideas from a German baby cookbook. I really liked foods like potato-carrot-steak, broccoli-parsnip-oats, tomato-zucchini-salmon, home-made pesto to introduce different nuts and spinach-whole grain pasta-salmon. Those were the flavors my daughters really liked. With time, I started introducing some soft finger foods like hard-boiled egg, avocado, tofu, whole grain pasta, or other pastas you could find, like black bean or lentil, and an omelet with yogurt mixed in. I introduced fruits in combination with oats or quinoa flakes to remove some of the sweetness and cooked them with whole milk.

My pediatrician told me to hold off on cow's milk and wait until they were one year old, but in Germany it is commonly used to cook oats and grains for the baby's dinner. Over time, I made the purees chunkier and then transitioned to finger foods altogether. It helps the children practice their pincer grasp where they can hold something between their thumb and pointing finger. Both my daughters eventually did not want to be fed anymore at around 7 to 8 months, but wanted to feed themselves and they ate more food that way. When babies transition to eating finger foods, or eat what everyone else is eating at the table, it makes it easier in the sense you don't have to worry about two different meals anymore, just making one. The key is not to season the food when you cook it, but first cook the food, take some of it off for the baby, and then adding some salt and/or other strong spices to the food for yourself. Babies should first be introduced to how foods taste naturally and not the sweet or salty enhanced flavors, otherwise they will choose those over the now perceived 'bland' tasting, unseasoned food.

Once babies start eating solids, it is also a good time to introduce water in a sippy cup to flush down the food. Try to not offer them too much water initially because babies can get filled up from the water and won't eat enough solids. Learning how to drink from a cup is usually accompanied by having puddles on the tray or table where the baby eats. Naturally, your baby will want to investigate what this is and add another level to the mess. On bad days, it is easier to give your baby a bath after eating than trying to clean them up with wipes. Cleaning after eating is not fun, but it is important for babies to touch the food and try to eat it themselves. They learn so much from being hands on and discover independence earlier on.

If you want to introduce foods to your baby that might otherwise be considered a choking hazard, you can get a feeding pacifier. They look like big pacifiers with holes in them and you can fill them with any food. The babies can chew on them and get the food mashed up before sucking it out, removing the choking hazard. We specifically liked those for berries and chunks of fruit, but also for teething. We filled them with fruits they really liked, then put them in the freezer. When our daughters had teething pain, we brought them out and they could chew on them, bringing them relief while also giving them refreshing and healthy fruits.

When our daughters were still eating purees and we were out and about and didn't want to deal with messy eating and bringing a container and spoon, we brought pouches of food. Stores sell them with pre-made food, but we purchased reusable pouches we would fill with our cooked puree. They loved them because the pouch itself was a fun way to eat, and they saw it as a treat.

We are true believers that picky eaters are made, not born. We made it our mission to cook a great variety of foods from different countries, exposing them to as many different flavors as possible. This way, we avoided them becoming picky eaters. If you encourage an open mind about all food, as they get older, they can become great eaters. Babies are naturally curious, and if you encourage this, you will be surprised what they end up liking. It is normal for them not to like everything though. This could be not only because of the flavor, but also because of the consistency. They might not care for purees, but prefer the texture of non-pureed foods. Paying attention to this can turn eating time from frustration into happy eating.

In the end, you have to find your own way of feeding your baby. Take what you learn about the feeding process as guidance, but not as a rule. Adjust it to your baby's needs and enjoy exploring with them together. If you don't like cooking or don't have the time to cook special food for your baby, then the glass jar foods are a good option. There are even delivery services who will cater to your very personal/specific needs and preferences with subscription boxes. If you prefer making all the food yourself, then have fun and don't take it personally if they spit it out. You will make it to the point where they feed themselves and you can enjoy a meal with your partner at the same time again without having to put most of your attention on your baby. One milestone down for now, in the next chapter we will continue to look at some more milestones to expect within the first year.

Memory Box

Take Pictures and a Video of Baby Eating Their First Solids

Write Down Your Baby's Favorite Foods at Certain Stages

Write Down a Recipe You Want to Pass On

Keep Their First Spoon or Real Silverware

_____

_____

_____

_____

_____

_____

_____

_____

_____

Baby's Milestones

In the last chapter, we discussed everything around eating, including one important milestone the baby reaches in their first year: eating solids. What are some other major milestones you will experience with your baby? Let's take a look at those important moments and what consequences they might have. This list does not include all developmental milestones, just the more memorable ones. Keep in mind that all babies develop at their own pace. Timelines given in this chapter are based on 'an average.' If your baby takes longer to reach a certain milestone, it does not mean there is a developmental issue. They just learn things at their own pace, which is perfectly normal.

With both our daughters, we truly had a great time watching them grow up and see their development. Sometimes it seemed like from one day to another something changed and a new skill was learned. We had milestone cards that showed the different occasions which we could use to take a picture or just keep them for the memory box. It was exciting to bring out a new card, add the date to it, and write down a couple memories of that event. At the same time, it was very interesting to see how differently my daughters achieved their milestones. Some milestones were reached more or less at the same time, but others showed a huge gap. For example, my older daughter rolled from her belly onto her back in her fifth month, my second one in her third month. Do these milestones make a big difference in the long run? I don't think so. Nevertheless, I was always thrilled when a new milestone was reached because it forced me to take a step back and realize how fast they were growing up. It was a useful reminder to me to always be in the moment and take it all in. The first year goes by so fast and the babies change so much during this time. My husband would periodically tell me in that current moment, our daughters were the smallest we would ever see them again!

Cherishing such milestones made me more appreciative of that reality. With our first daughter, we could not wait to see when she would hit the next milestone while trying to encourage her to get there. It always seemed to take forever for her to develop to the next stage. With our second one, time seemed to go by much faster and she seemed to jump from one milestone to the next without taking a 'proper' break. When I looked back at my older daughter's development, I realized she also developed fast, but having only one child to focus on gave us the time to really appreciate every moment of her growing up. Compared to our second one, at times it felt like she always had to share the attention with her older sibling. We made it our mission to give her extra attention whenever possible, and to support her development equally as much, even when it meant things would take longer or were a little more inconvenient. Once her older sister had matured a little more, she even had her own cheerleader while narrating and applauding all the new things she would do. For both our daughters, hitting their milestones was always a cause for celebration and we all enjoyed them together. After your baby is born and you get over the first shocking phase, you realize babies are actually pretty boring in the beginning. They eat, fill their diapers, and sleep most of the time. This is perfect because it gives you the chance to recover and rest as well. Babies have their awake phases, but they cannot do anything yet, so it gives you the opportunity to cuddle with your baby and enjoy skin-to-skin time with them. Enjoy it as long as it lasts because once they get more active, they might not care much for it anymore when they are awake. Besides that, you give your baby a bath about two times a week or as needed. More than twice a week could be the case if your baby has cradle cap, other skin issues, or is very soiled from a diaper explosion.

At first it will be a so-called "sponge bath," meaning you will wipe down your baby with a wet cloth to clean them. They will still have their umbilical cord attached and it should not get submerged in water. Simply clean around the umbilical cord and make sure it looks normal; meaning no redness or bad smell that could point towards an infection. The umbilical cord also gets in the way when changing diapers. You fold them over a bit to not irritate the cord and are careful to not rub on it. Don't worry too much about it now; you will have multiple opportunities to become an expert under the watchful supervision of the medical team. When the umbilical cord finally comes off, it is one of the first welcomed milestones. This happens between one and three weeks after birth. Finally, no more worries about accidentally plucking it off when it is barely hanging on to the belly button. Now you can give your baby 'real' baths, which is exciting. Most babies enjoy being in the water and it relaxes them. Pay attention to the temperature as their skin is still more sensitive, and ensure they are always supervised. Even with very little water in the bathtub, babies can still drown.

During their first month, babies will also start making other sounds than just crying. They make cute little sounds not only when they are awake, but also during their sleep. Sometimes you can even catch a glimpse of a little smile in their sleep or a clue to their personality. The first real smile they give you happens around two months and is so heartwarming. It finally feels like they are giving you love back. During the second month, they also start holding their head up for a short period of time when they lay on their belly. Babies now also follow you with their eyes, which makes it much more obvious how alert they are. After another month, you will hear one of the most beautiful sounds you can hear, your baby's laugh. This starts the fun period of finding out how to entertain your baby to make them laugh more. It can be just as amusing watching your partner becoming a clown to trigger another giggle, as hearing your baby's laugh. After three months, your baby might have also rolled over from their belly to their back on their own. Now that they can roll, they need a little more space, so make sure to not have anything that could hurt them laying right next to them, also including possible choking hazards.

At four months old, your baby can now grasp objects. At this point, parents with long hair should consider ponytails if they don't want accidental hair pulling! Necklaces and glasses also seem very interesting to the baby and might come off if not caught in time. It is very surprising how strong these little hands are and how far those short arms can extend. Their legs are also much stronger now and can support their body weight. They are still a few months away from standing on their own, though. At this age, babies also coo when you talk to them and enjoy playing peek-a-boo. You don't have to get fancy with blankets, you can just cover your eyes and uncover them and this will already bring them great joy.

Some babies will also start teething around this age, even though most get their first tooth later. First signs of teething are usually increased drooling and fussiness. They will also bite whatever they can get in their hands to get some relief. How your baby handles teething really depends on their pain tolerance level. My first daughter got fussy, therefore at night we gave her some Tylenol and she slept through the night. She got one tooth at a time, and usually at least a few days in between each new tooth. My second daughter did not handle it so well. She was crying much more, and the Tylenol did not seem to bring her much relief. Per her pediatrician's guidance, we had to upgrade to ibuprofen, which really helped her. One week she was doing particularly badly, waking up three times a night because she had three new teeth coming in over the course of three days. Luckily, there are some helpful products that do not require medication.

Both of them enjoyed bite rings that were cooled in the refrigerator. You may also find the teething gels you can put on the gums to create a numbing feeling, but be aware they are not recommended anymore.

Once the first tooth is exposed, you take on a new responsibility: brushing this one tooth. Proper dental hygiene from a young age is important. Brushing their gums also helps with relieving some of the pressure pain they experience before their teeth become exposed.

When your baby is five months old, expect more laughter and squealing from happiness. When they lay on their bellies, they can hold their heads up high and steady while pushing their chest up. They support raising up their chest with their arms. This will make them roll over much more. They now also focus on smaller objects and try to reach for them. Sometime between now and six months of age, the baby will also eat their first solids. One not so pleasant milestone is the 'stranger danger' anxiety, as it is accompanied by crying. Overall, it is a good thing; they recognize who they know and can trust. It can feel a little bit embarrassing to parents though, when family or friends come over who haven't seen the baby yet, are super excited, but when they first meet the baby, they are confronted with a crying little human who is not equally as excited about meeting them. Especially for family members, this can be hurtful. If your baby is showing signs of this, it is a good solution to prepare your visitors for this behavior and reassure them it is not because the baby doesn't like them, but because the baby doesn't know them. After spending some time together and when the baby sees how you interact with people, they warm up and will happily be carried around and get extra attention. It will be easier for your guests to face the initial crying, knowing it has nothing to do with them, but is a normal developmental stage of all babies.

When your baby is six months old, you realize they are now halfway through their first year. Where did the time go? At this time, your baby rolls not only from belly to back, but from back to belly as well. This opens up more space for them to move around. Some babies roll through the room, others lay on their bellies and turn in circles, pushing themselves backwards until they get to where they want to be. To make sure your house is baby proofed, get down on your knees or lay on your belly and look around. You might see some dangerous areas you missed before because you were too far up.

Your baby can now also sit down with support and enjoy the new view. When your baby is lying down on their belly, they will extend their arms. Now that your baby is eating solids, it is also a good time to introduce the sippy cup. Between four to six months, the first tooth comes in. It looks small, but it is very sharp. Beware of your fingers ending up in your baby's mouth. When they are teething, they like to bite on objects to relieve the pain and unfortunately, your finger is also a very nice option for them! Another option for them to bite on is the nipple while breastfeeding. Ouch!!! This is very painful and if you end up with a wound, try to change the feeding position to not aggravate the damaged area additionally. There are special creams you can put on your nipple to aid the healing process that are completely safe for your baby to consume during the next feeding. Now that the first tooth is exposed, you need to start good brushing habits. We initially used the silicone finger brush with only water. Toothpaste comes along around one year, after their first visit to the dentist. However, at this age, they luckily enjoy the toothbrush as it helps them with their teething discomfort.

At seven months old, your baby sees in full color, and their hearing is fully developed. They are very curious and enjoy exploring new environments. They imitate sounds and can have a small 'conversation' with you, which might make them laugh as well. When you play peek-a-boo with a cloth with them, you might be surprised they now can cover their eyes on their own with the cloth and pull it down, getting very happy and excited when they hear the peek-a-boo as soon as they spot you again. They also like to clap and try out making new sounds. At seven months old your baby can push themselves up into the crawling position and might even start crawling. If you don't have an area gated off for them to protect themselves from moving to dangerous locations like stairs, then they need constant supervision to make sure they don't get themselves in trouble. They continue to explore by putting objects in their mouth, so keep their arm's reach in mind. This also counts for food. Your baby can now feed themselves with big enough, soft finger foods.

When your baby is eight months old, they move around crawling quite fast now, so, try to keep up! Your baby will also sit up unassisted now. The transition from sitting to lying down can be a little rough and it will be easier for them if the surrounding area is not too cluttered or covered in hard or sharp objects like wooden blocks. By now, you must have said your baby's name hundreds of times, but now your baby actually responds to their name. They can pass objects between their hands and instead of using a raking movement to pick up objects, they can pick them up using the thumb and index finger.

At nine months old, your baby is much more vocal, speaks baby talk, and can understand short, easy phrases like "no-no" and "bye-bye." You might even get lucky enough if they wave at you at the same time. Your baby might cling to you more when seeing strangers and perhaps hiding their face. When your baby drops a toy, they will actually look for it. When they have a toy in their hand, they bang it and throw it. Try to show your baby their reflection in a mirror as they now can identify themselves in mirrors.

When your baby is ten months old, they should be able to finger feed themselves much better. Your baby is strong enough now to pull themselves up to a standing position. A couch is usually the perfect height. Now their reach extends even further and you have to pay attention to what you leave lying around on surfaces. Many times, a phone, laptop, or a book ends up on the couch and this is very interesting for your baby. They pull the objects towards them, bite them, throw them, drop them and rip them. Whatever you value should now be put on even higher surfaces. Make sure snacks are out of reach as well. Not only might they contain ingredients your baby should not be eating yet, but they can also pose choking hazards.

At eleven months old, your baby starts cruising along furniture to move around, standing up on their feet. When they get to the end of the piece of furniture, you can even see them stand unsupported. They now recognize objects and point at them. Your baby might even put an object into a container. They also prefer repetitive sounds and respond to them compared to non-repetitive sounds.

Congratulations, the big outstanding milestone is now your baby's first birthday! They might be walking already. If they are, then get ready for a workout. Your one-year-old has tons of energy to burn, and sometimes keeping up with them can seem like a challenge. Your baby can now sit for long periods of time and can pick up small objects with the pincer grasp. They might even surprise you with another word or two, even if they are made-up words (in my daughter's case, it was "nana" for milk). Your baby now imitates other people's activities and understands simple instructions. Your baby's brain has doubled in size, and you can already get a glimpse of the personality your baby develops. During your baby's first year, they might have also gotten their first haircut and probably have gotten sick for the first time.

In the course of your baby's first year, they also experience special days like Valentine's Day, Easter, Mother's Day, Father's Day, Thanksgiving, Christmas, and the New Year. These are only a few of the most common days. Depending on your background, there might be other days added, or you might not celebrate the days mentioned. With our daughters being half German, we also celebrate Fasching (carnival), Oktoberfest, St. Martin, Nikolaus Day, and Advent Sundays, to name a few special days for us.

No matter when your baby hits their milestones, it is always a good reason to take a step back and enjoy the moment with them, now realizing how fast they grow up and develop. Don't compare your child to others of the same age. Every baby develops differently, and if a baby develops fast and hits milestones early, it does not mean they will be 'smarter or better' than your own child. It is not a competition for your baby to achieve certain milestones faster than others. They are on their own schedule and will get to them when they are ready. Rather, focus on being ready yourself when they reach them!

Now that we have a broad overview of the biggest milestones, we will look at an important part of your child's development: speaking and communication.

Memory Box

Take Pictures with Milestone Cards

Keep Umbilical Cord

Take Pictures of the Special Moments

Keep Their Favorite Stuffed Animal

Keep Their Favorite Toy

Keepsakes From Special Events

_____

_____

_____

_____

_____

_____

_____

_____

Communication and Speaking with Your Baby

In the previous chapter, we looked at some of the milestones during your baby's first year. One of the milestones mentioned was their first words. Communication with your baby is very important to set a good baseline for the future. Now you might wonder what is the best way to talk to your baby? Is it not necessary to talk to them when they are infants and do not understand what you are saying?

When I initially held my first daughter in my arms, I was overwhelmed. I was very happy and excited, but at the same time I didn't know how to hold her correctly and was afraid I would hurt her. I could just look at her and try to soothe her repeatedly with a loving "yes." That is when my husband told me to talk to her. I pulled a blank and actually thought about what I should tell her. What is the right thing to say? It felt awkward with the first few words because I thought she did not understand what I was saying, so why should I stress her out more?

When I overcame this initial sense of awkwardness, I kept talking to her in German. The nurses looked at me a little surprised but didn't say anything. After I had my talking time with my daughter, it was my husband's turn to take over, and she was showered in Spanish declarations of love. The nurses looked at us even more surprised. When it was time for the doctors or nurses to check up on the baby, they spoke to her in English. This set the stage for our daughter's journey to be raised trilingual. We knew I would speak to her in German, my husband in Spanish, and through conversations between my husband and I, or with friends and through daycare, she would learn English. When our second daughter was born, there was no initial shyness and the talking came naturally. Overall, when people around us found out our daughters would be raised trilingual, we received many questions, if we were not overwhelming our children, and perhaps this was too much for them to handle. In Europe, it is quite normal and encouraged for children to grow up multi-lingual. In the US, it is a skill-set not readily appreciated. All the research we had done previously suggested three languages would not be an issue. Family and friends accepted that, or not, who cares... and were just curious to see how this would all work out in the end. We knew most likely our children would start speaking a little bit later than other children of the same age, knowing fewer words of one language, but they eventually would be able to understand and communicate in three languages.

During our research, we also learned babies and children can get frustrated when you don't understand what they are saying. Thinking about that with ours, the level of frustration might be even higher, we decided to also introduce a few hand signs to be able to communicate the most important things with them before they would be able to speak. We decided on milk, water, food, more, and all done. We would show the hand signs while speaking to them and repeat them over and over for them to understand what we meant. After some time, they were able to request these things before they were able to speak to us. We were very consistent with speaking to them in our native languages, even when there were other people around who didn't understand us. If you have the conviction to raise your child multilingually, do not apologize for it. You will be surprised how many people wish they were given that opportunity. We explained to them what was going on so they wouldn't feel disrespected or that we were being rude, but sometimes we still got weird looks. In the end, it all worked out because both our daughters responded to what we told them in our languages and they could follow what we told them. This way they learn three languages the easiest way possible, and it will be an easier transition for them if they want to learn more languages in the future.

No matter if you want to raise your baby multilingual or not, it is important to speak and sing to them. You might think they don't understand what's going on or cannot comprehend what you are saying, but your baby is like a sponge, absorbing everything around them from the moment they are born. They love hearing your voice and can tell from your tone if this is a happy conversation or not. Do not hold back when you talk to your baby. If you don't know what exactly to talk about, then look around and tell them everything you see, smell, hear, and feel. Tell them about the world around them. Babies naturally like high-pitched voices, which mimic female voices. It comforts them and will not interfere with learning how to speak properly. Once they start babbling and making more sounds, you can have a 'conversation' with them.

When they talk to you (initially, just some sounds) let them finish their babbling, look them in the eyes and smile at them. When they are done, respond to them. This teaches them an important lesson: what they say is important to you. This encourages them to keep speaking. When they speak to you, try to repeat what they say even if it is "da-da" or "ga-ga." You might not know what they are saying, but it will make them speak more, rather than give up and be quiet. Babies learn speaking by imitating what they hear. The more you speak to them, the more chances they have to repeat. When they are old enough to see the world around them, you can show them objects and describe them. Repetition is key, as it will take time for them to learn and remember everything. They will also understand much more of what you say, than what they can speak. So don't underestimate their level of comprehension. They might surprise you. Initially, try to keep the sentences short and easy. Incorporate singing as well, this is another form of soothing them.

Your baby does not care if you can sing well or not, they much rather enjoy your performance and love the sound of your voice, so no judging at all. Even with the sentences being short and easy, this does not mean you need to adjust the words you say. You don't need to add a "y" at the end of a word to make it sound cute ("Look at the ducky") and you don't need to generalize everything. Although baby words might sound sweet and fun, be careful not to teach them the wrong vocabulary. Teach them the specific words, such as the tiger and lion, not just referring to them as "big cats." Yes, you might have to repeat the words a few more times for them to remember, but there is no need to limit their vocabulary. Vocabulary is improved by word exposure at this age... the more the better.

It will take some time for your baby to start saying their first words. If you want to enable them to communicate with sign language, you can find plenty of good information online about how to start, when to start, and many videos will show you exactly how to do each sign. This is if you want to stick to the 'official' sign language. If you want to teach a limited number of words, you can also make up your own signs, but then you need to keep in mind no one else will know the signs but you. That can cause frustration in daycare if your baby is trying to communicate, but the providers don't know the made-up signs. Babies as young as six months can communicate a few signs to show their needs. They get so excited when they realize you understand what they say. Our daughters took longer, but still signaled with hand gestures months before they actually talked. We started introducing the signs once we introduced solids.

We would show them the sign for water while saying water a few times and showing them the sippy cup until they understood it. Eventually they would make the sign to request the water themselves and each sign they did felt like a mini celebration. It brought down the frustration levels on both sides as well. For some parents, sign language works, for others, not so much. For us it made sense for the basic needs, but not the entire language.

Others introduce many signs, and the rest skip it all together. This is really based on personal preference.

Have you considered raising your baby multilingually? The world has become so connected and open, you can go to the supermarket and hear ten different languages during this trip. You might have friends from different countries and backgrounds and start thinking that speaking more than one language fluently is not a bad idea. It has certainly made travel more memorable and opened professional opportunities for us. If you took language classes during high school, you know how hard it can be to learn a language when you are older. The easiest way to learn a language is by being raised in a language. Maybe you or your partner have a native language different from English. This is the easiest way to teach your baby a second language. You just start speaking to them in this language from birth on, and they will learn to understand it and speak it as easily as English. If both parents speak different languages, then go for both, your baby will still learn English at daycare and/or in their immediate environment.

The number one key factor is that you must be consistent. Once you decide to raise your child in a different language, you have to stick with it, not only at home, but also when you go out, or are around other people who don't speak your language. If you switch to English when outside of the house and switch to your language when you are back home, your child gets confused. Yes, they might learn and understand it, but what happens many times is you tell them something in your language and they end up answering in English. Make sure you insist on them answering in your language. Initially, they mix up the languages and choose whatever word is the easiest before they learn to differentiate between the languages and know which parent to approach in which language. It might be uncomfortable speaking to your child in another language when there are only English speakers around and you don't want to seem rude. What worked for me was letting them know I was speaking German with my children and I will not break this routine, so people knew I wasn't gossiping behind their back. If someone had a problem with it, then too bad. I care about my children knowing all their native languages way more than making strangers or others around me happy and comfortable. I figured if people had a problem with it and weren't supportive, then they didn't care about my cultural background and heritage much, so they were likely not worth the effort as far as I was concerned.

Some parents have a different native language, but decide for their children not to learn it and only be raised speaking English. Every person I have met who was raised that way has told me they wish their parents would have taught them their native language. Many have attempted to learn it as adults, but had a hard time mastering it and might still have an accent. They not only saw it as a wasted opportunity for them to know another language fluently, but also felt like they were denied another access point in getting to know the culture of the parent's country. Knowing another language opens up an entirely new world you would never have experienced without knowing the language.

You don't have to be a native speaker of a different language to raise your child multilingual. You might decide you want your baby to learn another language, but if neither parent speaks another language, what is the best way to go about it? There are several options you can explore. You can look into finding a daycare provider who speaks to the children in a different language. You can also try to find a nanny who has a different native background and can speak to your baby in their language. A third option would be an au pair. If you have a preference of what language you want your children to learn, you can choose the country they come from with certain au pair programs. It might feel strange to you that your child will know another language you don't understand, but you can either try to learn the basics of that language as well, or just be ok with it. You not knowing a different language should not keep your child from getting ahead in their future, and the younger they are, the easier it is to learn a new language.

Whatever decision you make concerning how you teach your children to speak-with sign language or without, with different languages, or just one language; what matters the most is being patient with them and repeating everything you say over and over so they learn. Encourage them when they start talking "baby" to you, so they feel heard and can have a conversation with you. Even though it might seem unnecessary because they cannot speak yet, you are laying the foundation for their communication skills later on in their lives. Plus, your baby loves hearing your voice, so keep talking to them!

We have focused on many aspects of your baby and their upbringing at home, and the common environment. Having a baby usually means you are settling down. It does not mean you cannot see the world anymore, so let's see how your baby affects traveling in the next chapter.

Memory Box

Note Your Baby's First Word

Note Your Baby's First Sign

Write Down the Lyrics of Your Baby's Favorite Song

Your Baby's Favorite Book

Recording of Your Baby's Adorable Voice

_____

_____

_____

_____

_____

_____

_____

_____

_____

Travel the World

In the last chapter, we discussed your baby learning how to speak and looked at the possibility of introducing another language early on. Knowing another language can be very useful in the future for traveling as well. Many people think when they have children, they have to settle down and give up most or all of the fun things they did before. Even though you have to adjust to living your life with children, it does not mean you have to give up everything, and you can still see the world. Even if you have not traveled much before having your baby, read on for tips on how to make the most of these wonderful opportunities together.

One of our favorite pursuits for both my husband and me is traveling and seeing the world. We have made it a goal to see at least one new country every year, as we are passionate about discovering the world. This passion did not vanish after the babies. Quite the opposite. Their arrival made us want to share this joy with them. With his family living in California and my family living in Germany, it was always a given that in order for us to see family, we would have to get on the plane and take a long trip to be able to spend time with them. We both knew when we had children, we wanted them to have a connection with our families. It was very important to me that my daughters grow up embracing both cultures of their two home countries. You only truly get to know the culture of a country when you spend time there, so the deal was every year we would fly to Germany and spend time there. Right after they were born, we applied for their American and German passports. When our first daughter was 2½ months old, we flew to Germany for her to meet her family, and also met up with my brother-in-law and his family in Portugal. At four months old, we took her to Colombia and Peru. We discovered that traveling with an infant was very encouraging and actually one of the best times to travel, as the baby is not mobile and added accommodations are minimum.

Right as we were flying back, the pandemic hit and traveling internationally was restricted. We adjusted and took trips by car to uncrowded places, such as farms, mountains, and the greater outdoors. This was the first year we did not fly to Germany, and it really upset me. I got pregnant again and the following year, my husband and I both got vaccinated against COVID-19 early on, and decided to take a trip to Aruba. We spent our honeymoon there ten years earlier, so the plan had always been to go back there to celebrate our anniversary. Expecting our second daughter one month before our anniversary, we did an early anniversary trip and went while I was six months pregnant. Six weeks after my second daughter was born, we flew to Germany as restrictions were finally lifted. Once in Germany, we also did a trip to Croatia, Bosnia and Herzegovina, and Montenegro. We stayed in an apartment and drove everywhere, keeping our distance from people. Back home, we did a few trips by car in the area. In the near future, we will travel to Germany again and visit Malta, another country in Europe we haven't seen, and we are planning a trip to South America. And next year? Who knows, the world is so large and full of exciting possibilities.

We have learned that for traveling, we need to always pack certain items, whereas others get adjusted, depending on the style of travel and the destination. We learned to pack a bit more lightly for us to have space for the girls' clothes and diapers. Things we always packed for them were clothes, a sleeping bag and pajamas, their favorite stuffed animal or toy, Tylenol for pain and fever, shampoo and a washcloth, hand sanitizer and sanitizing wipes. In the diaper backpack we had enough diapers and wipes for the travel portion of the trip, a changing mat, doggy bags for the dirty diapers or dirty clothes, a second or even third outfit in case there was a diaper explosion, a burp cloth, a swaddle when they were little, a carrier, the water bottle and snacks, and new toys. We decided to always pack enough diapers for the entire trip so: 1) we wouldn't have to worry about finding a store with diapers immediately, 2) we didn't have to worry about potential sizing differences that impact fit and comfort levels, and 3) this method allows us to free up space in our luggage to bring home souvenirs.

Travel will be most successful when you take your time to plan ahead. Sit down and talk about different scenarios and write down a list of things to verify and pack, so as not to forget anything. When traveling by car, look at the entire travel time and decide before you leave where you want to build-in stops for feeding and to give your baby some time to move around. Clearly this is assuming your baby is on a regular sleep schedule. Plan for some buffer time in case your baby wakes up more often, or needs more time outside the car seat. Be aware of the space you have in the car to pack luggage on top of the stroller, or even a travel crib. You might have to pack less than you thought in order to fit everything. Keep in mind the weather conditions as well. In case you have an emergency, you won't have any issues with your baby being cold or wet, for example. Try to figure out where you will change diapers as well, especially if you have to pull over somewhere with no restroom facilities available. Plan for enough formula, food and water for the baby, and for yourself, in order to not have to find a restaurant at a certain time in an unknown location. The goal is to be self-reliant during the course of driving.

Traveling by plane adds another layer of unknowns to your plan because you depend on others, like the airport staff or other travelers, for everything to go smoothly. Preparation for a successful flight starts with planning as well. Have everything packed the day before you fly so you don't have to worry about a last-minute hectic rush. A big factor to make a flight successful is the time of the flight. If you can align the flight time with nap time, you might be lucky enough to have a sleeping baby during the flight. When you decide on a flight, make sure you have enough time before the flight leaves to take care of everything. Keep in mind the time you need to arrive at the airport. Make sure to factor in extra time for handling your baby at the airport.

Your baby still wants to be fed and changed when they feel like it. Going through security will take more time as well. Rushing through the airport with a baby usually results in stressed parents and a crying baby. Both combined are not a good way to begin your trip! When you arrive at the airport with enough time on your hands, you can check in your luggage and your car seat. The first car seat is usually free. If your stroller allows for the car seat to be attached, this is one less thing to worry about. You can use the stroller until it is time to board the airplane, which makes everything much more comfortable.

When you go through security you usually cannot bring any water or liquids in great quantities. This is different when it comes to your baby. It is possible to bring a water bottle for the baby or pumped breast milk through security, as well as food pouches. When it is time to board the plane, families with babies usually can enter first to have some extra time to get settled in. You can take the stroller all the way to the entrance door of the plane, where airport staff will store it in the plane. After landing, it will be returned to you at the door of the plane. Flying with an infant can be done in two different ways: you can either carry your baby on your lap or you can request a bassinet for your baby to sleep in. If you want a bassinet, which is usually possible on longer flights, you will have to reserve it before you start the flight.

Whenever you book your tickets, follow up with a phone call to the airline to make sure you can get a seat that allows for a bassinet to be attached. Only very specific seats have this option, so you need to make sure there is availability beforehand. Takeoff is a good time to feed the baby or give them a pacifier to help with ear pressure relief. Drinking or eating motions naturally help clear their ears. Be ready to cuddle with your baby, they might look for more comfort while going through all this unfamiliar excitement. Once you are in the air the next challenge arises: you need to change the baby's diaper. The toilets in the airplanes have changing tables stowed away above the toilet that you can fold out. This leaves you with little extra space in an already small restroom. To avoid having to take a big diaper bag into the tiny restroom, we pack a small pouch that fits three diapers and a thin pack of wipes. Added to that are two plastic bags for any accidents and a small pack of sanitizing wipes. When I changed my baby's diaper I placed the portable folded changing mat under my arm, the small pouch in one hand, allowing me to comfortably carry the baby. That way I could easily unfold the table, put the changing mat on top, lay the baby down, then open up the pouch. If I needed more diapers during the flight, I could refill them from the diaper backpack afterwards.

Sometimes you see parents change their baby's diapers in their seats. This of course is much more comfortable for the parent, but in my opinion, inconsiderate towards the other passengers and should be avoided out of courtesy. Besides that, you just have to wait until the flight is over and make your baby happy during the flight. Smaller babies usually have an easier time traveling than bigger ones. Once they start sitting, crawling and moving around more, maybe even walking, it is more difficult to let them have the exercise they would like. The younger they are, the easier it is to travel on a plane with them.

When you board a flight with a baby, you can usually expect some unhappy looks from passengers around you. Their fear is that your baby will cry the entire flight and make everyone around them miserable. This is especially true for long flights when people want to sleep. Don't take it personally, and don't let it get you nervous or stressed out. What helps is to bring additional earplugs or small chocolates to offer those around you. Most of the passengers will be pleasantly surprised about how well your baby will do during the flight. It is usually the toddlers who cause more trouble and make more noise. Try to ignore the other passengers and focus on yourself and the baby and enjoy the flight. After all, they booked a flight with over one hundred other people on the plane, not a private jet! You will probably never see these people again, so focus on the things that matter.

When it's time for landing, offer food or something to drink again to clear your baby's ears. You have officially overcome the hardest part of the trip. Now it is just immigration (if it is an international flight), getting your luggage, and then off to enjoy your stay.

Once it is time to enjoy your vacation, be ready for some fun. Sharing a trip with your baby is a whole new experience and makes it very special. Don't limit yourself. You can still see the world and enjoy it. You will most likely adjust your travel experience compared to what you did before. What definitely has to adjust are the expectations of everything you want to do and see now that your baby is tagging along. Plan whatever you would like to do and once you have a good idea, cut this in half and you end up more or less with what you will be able to do. The pace of traveling changes because you have to do more stops and plan around feedings and diaper changes, naps and teething pain. Some things you won't be able to do because you cannot bring a baby along, therefore you will explore places you haven't considered before because they didn't fit your lifestyle without children. This already starts with making the decision of where you want to travel. Is it worth going to the places that are usually known as more dangerous or do you rather go somewhere that is known to be safe and family friendly? Party area, nature, or resort? It continues with the accommodation. You might have always enjoyed staying at a hotel, but since there is a baby involved, does it make more sense to get an apartment instead?

We have learned to enjoy space and comfort over the convenience of hotels, but this is different for everyone. For us, an important factor to consider is access to healthcare. In case anything happens, we want to have fast and easy access to good doctors and clinics to ensure our daughters would be well taken care of in case of an emergency. That means the rainforest trip to the Amazon, where your survival kit includes antidotes against certain snake poison, is off the table for the moment, but there are so many other things to see in the world, it doesn't really matter.

One thing to keep in mind when you travel are the different cultures. Try to get an understanding of what awaits you and what is considered normal or rude in the country you visit. Whereas in some countries people look at your baby from a distance and leave it at that, in other countries it is completely normal for the women to approach you and want to carry your baby. You can be easily caught off guard when you don't know what to expect, so try to find out some information before finding yourself in a situation you would have preferred to avoid. Another challenge can be going out to eat with your baby. Going out once in a while on your timeline works out just fine, but when you travel and eat out often, pay attention to the time factor. If everything is booked out already and you have to wait until a later time to eat, you might get serenaded with your baby's cries because you go past their normal bedtime. A nonromantic solution to this problem is to divide and conquer. One parent tries to soothe the baby while the other one eats, then you switch. It can be helpful to plan a few nights ahead and make reservations or go out for dinner a little bit earlier than usual to avoid having to push your baby's bedtime too late.

Overall, no matter how sweet and angelic your baby is, prepare yourself for at least one day of your trip for your baby to ruin all your plans. Make this day a more relaxed one by putting your baby into focus again, and continue exploring the following day. Overall, babies are great travel partners. They either sleep or are curious to discover this new world. It can be a nice memory to hire a photographer to capture some family pictures. You will notice that pictures these days are either just the baby or the baby and one parent. Treating yourself with someone else taking the pictures and the entire family being in them together can be a great way to add another special touch to your trip. Even if the baby cries during the photoshoot, this just captures another facet of life with them, so it is still worth it.

Traveling with your baby will not only allow you to continue seeing the world and enjoy what you love doing, but it also sets the right mindset for your child in the future. If you are unsure about certain aspects of the trip, talk to someone who has done it before and get some input. Don't let the one person with only negative experiences ruin it for you. Do your research, prepare, and enjoy yourself!

You will need all the relaxation and calm you can get for when your baby gets sick for the first time, discussed in the next chapter.

Memory Box

Souvenirs of the Trip

Family Pictures

Gift for Baby from the Airline

First Flight Ticket

Buy Something Special for Your Baby to Gift Them
When They are Older

Their First Post Card

_____

_____

_____

_____

_____

_____

_____

Baby's First Illnesses

In the last chapter, we talked about tips and tricks for traveling with your baby and having a good and relaxing time. This chapter focuses on the opposite: when your baby gets sick. We will look at some common first illnesses and how to deal with them. This list is not extensive, but covers what most parents will eventually see their babies go through.

When our first daughter was born, I took excellent care of myself to not get sick and stay strong and healthy, in order to take care of her. The first scare we had one week after her umbilical cord fell off: she bled from her belly button. We called the doctor immediately to get her seen and, in the end, it was most likely just some scab that was left over that had come off. It was nerve wracking nevertheless, because I realized I had no idea what was normal for a baby and what wasn't. When was it necessary to go to the clinic, and when was it just overreacting? Besides that, she was quite healthy. She had a day here and there where she was a little gassy and her belly hurt around one month of age.

When we traveled to Germany at three months old, she got her first cold and was very congested. I tried my best to comfort her and let hot water sit in the sink to steam, while sitting next to the sink with her, which seemed to help a bit. When she finally fell asleep at night, she had a normal night and was better the next day. At ten months old, she started going to daycare. On the second day, she came home with a fever. I searched the internet to remind myself what temperature was the threshold to take her to the clinic, and was relieved to see she was well below that. After three days the fever was gone, but she had a bad rash on her back. We took her to the doctor, who said we just had to wait it out. Cleared that it wasn't anything contagious, she went back to daycare, just to come back with another fever a few days later. This time, we were more relaxed. After that she caught a cold.

Soon after, in spring, she started sneezing and had a runny nose. Back to the doctor, but this time around we learned she had an allergy to one of the plants in the daycare's backyard, or immediate surroundings. When she started solids at six months old, she seemed to get a little bit constipated. Once the teething started, she had teething pain. When she could crawl, she chased after our cats and loved pulling our Tomcat's paws and tail, which eventually led to him kicking her and even a scratch.

With our second daughter, things looked a little different. She had her first cold at three weeks old, passed on from her older sister after catching it at daycare. To deal with the congestion, I had to elevate the head end of her bassinet so she would not lie down completely flat. She had a few horrible nights with very little sleep, but she made it through. She got a few fevers over time, usually a free gift from her older sister's daycare. She also seemed to get a little bit constipated after starting solids, but got over it quickly. One night she vomited and threw up all the milk she had eaten twice in a row. I immediately got concerned she would get dehydrated if it happened again. Luckily, it was just a short episode and she was back to her normal hungry self when she woke up again. Her pain tolerance was much lower than my older daughter, so she struggled with the teething pain much more, many nights with interrupted sleep. Tylenol seemed to not help her, so we listened to her pediatrician and switched to ibuprofen. The pandemic added a whole new layer to the colds that my two daughters had. There was always the fear they had COVID-19. Since my younger daughter stayed home with me, it wasn't an issue for her, but my older daughter had to get tested for COVID-19 several times, and it was always painful to see her cry in the process. Luckily every single test came back negative. I was always fully aware of the fact that children get sick and they have to get sick in order to build up their immune system. Nevertheless, it was always difficult to see my daughters suffer and cry from pain or discomfort. There is nothing more difficult than seeing them feel sick and not being able to help them out immediately.

As a parent, you always want to protect your children and want the best for them. Therefore, when you see your baby sick and suffering, you feel very helpless and it can be scary to not know what is going on and what you can do to improve the situation. It is very common for babies to get sick as they come into contact with the world around them and build up their immune system. Especially once they start going to daycare or if they have older siblings, they seem to attract illnesses like magnets. It doesn't matter if they are three months old when they go to daycare or one year old, they will get sick just as often because they are exposed to many more new germs than at home. I was once told it is normal for your baby to get sick ten to fifteen times per year. Knowing that doesn't make it easier to handle, though. Very common illnesses are the cold or the three-day-fever, also known as roseola infantum. The three-day-fever symptoms are fever, as the name implies, for three days. Once the fever breaks and goes down, a rash appears. The rash usually lasts up to two days and disappears on its own. When your baby has a cold and their nose is runny, you can use saline spray and suction out the mucus to help with the breathing. You can also go into a bathroom with hot water turned on to increase humidity in the air. A humidifier in the nursery helps out as well. One home remedy passed down in the family is boiling eucalyptus leaves in water and then placing the pot mix in the nursery. This should only be done if it is not possible for the baby to reach the pot. If nothing helps, and your baby has a difficult time sleeping, you can try to elevate the bassinet or crib mattress on one end so the head is above the rest of the body.

Dealing with fever is its own topic. Fever is considered a rectal temperature of 100.4°F or higher. There is fever you can treat at home with Tylenol and there is a fever that is high enough you should take your baby to the doctor. There will be times as a parent you will not be sure about when to go to the doctor. As a parent, you tend to worry and make decisions based on emotions more so than rational thought. Find out if your pediatric clinic offers a nurse help line you can call before taking your baby in to be seen, or if the trip is even necessary. It can be very exhausting and stressful for you and the baby to take them to urgent care in the middle of the night, and having to wait for care for hours, just to find out you could have given them a dose of Tylenol.

If your baby is younger than three months old and has a fever, you should take them to a doctor. You should get your baby seen without having given them any medication. If your baby is between three and six months old, the magic number is 102°F. If the fever is over that threshold, take your baby to the doctor. If your baby's temperature is below that, but they seem sick, you need to take your baby in to be seen. Outside these instances, treat the fever at home. For a six to twenty-four months old baby, with a temperature higher than 102°F, that lasts longer than one day, but shows no other signs or symptoms, contact your health care provider. If your baby also shows other symptoms like a cold, cough, or diarrhea; contact your doctor sooner based on how your baby feels overall. In general, if your baby's fever lasts more than three days, contact your pediatrician. Ways to make your baby feel better when they have a fever are giving them Tylenol or ibuprofen to bring down the fever, give them a lukewarm bath, or remove extra clothing to avoid overheating. Dehydration is always a concern with fever, so make sure to offer liquids more frequently. Try to comfort your baby more, they usually get more needy when they don't feel well. Although it was once believed teething causes fevers, this has been proven wrong.

Besides the fever, vomiting and diarrhea can also cause dehydration in a baby. Vomiting is different from the normal spit up. Spit up is usually a smaller amount of milk that is still in liquid form, or already a little bit seedy when it has been somewhat processed. Vomiting is a bigger amount of milk or food and comes out more forcefully. If it happens just once, then keep an eye on your baby and offer liquids and more food later. When they keep it down, it is a good sign and you can move on. If your baby keeps vomiting, or does the so-called projectile vomiting, it is time to call the doctor. For diarrhea, the threshold is three times. If your baby has three consecutive watery stools, contact your doctor. Monitor the fluid intake of your baby during these times. Be aware of the number of wet diapers your baby produces over time. If the number drops down, your baby cries without tears, or seems in any other way 'drier,' this might be a sign of dehydration. Call your doctor to get guidance on treatment. Pedialyte is an option (electrolyte solution), but should always be discussed with a doctor first for babies under one year old.

Some young babies seem to cry for no reason and cannot be comforted. This can be a sign of colic. How do you distinguish colic from a gassy baby? Crying caused by colic is usually three hours or more per day, for three or more days per week, for three or more weeks. The crying usually peaks in the evening. It is most common in babies around six weeks old and declines by three to four months of age. Gassy babies, on the other hand, seem more bothered after feedings, after crying, or when they use a pacifier because they swallow air. The best way to help prevent gas discomfort is burping. Try moving your baby's legs in a bicycle motion or massage the belly. If you are feeding your baby with a bottle, try a different nipple with a slower flow.

Other visually obvious issues are rashes, eczema, and cradle cap. Rashes are not necessarily a reason to worry. Our older daughter had many rashes and dry skin when she was a baby. Our pediatrician said to put cortisone lotion on her, and that's what we did, and it helped most of the time. If a rash seems to be infected or does not get better within a few days, you should contact your doctor. Rashes usually clear up relatively quickly. In contrast to that, eczema is a long-term condition that needs to be treated. If your baby has what appears to be a rash and it does not go away after several days, it should be checked by a doctor to find out if it is eczema. It is usually itchy and irritated, and affects cheeks, forehead, and joints like elbows and knees. Should your baby be diagnosed with eczema, your doctor will discuss a treatment plan with you. It often involves (daily) baths, moisturizers, medicated lotions and removal of irritants. In contrast to eczema, cradle cap is much less itchy, and often appears as yellowish scales on the scalp. It can also spread to the eye area, nose and behind the ears. The scales become flaky over time and can be rubbed off, most easily during a bath with the help of special brushes. Cradle cap usually clears up before the baby's first birthday.

Another very common illness in babies are ear infections. They are less common in breastfed babies but can still happen. Common signs for an ear infection are baby's tugging their ears, fever, trouble sleeping, crying, fluid draining from the ear, problems with their balance, and problems with hearing. Many babies show symptoms of these signs as well when they are teething. For babies, it is difficult to locate where their pain is coming from when they are teething, so many times they pull their ears as well, are fussy, and have trouble sleeping. I remember being concerned many times that my daughter had an ear infection, but it always turned out to be teething. If you suspect your baby has an ear infection, call the doctor to schedule an in-person appointment to get a diagnosis.

Babies can develop allergies to food, environments, and animals, to name a few examples. When you introduce solids, start with one at a time to see how your baby reacts. If your baby develops a rash, belly pain, diarrhea or a runny nose, just to name a few of the symptoms, you can easily identify which food caused the reaction. There is no cure for food allergies, so make sure your baby stays away from whatever triggered their reaction.

Environmental/seasonal allergies show symptoms like runny or stuffy nose, sneezing or watery eyes. Animals, for example, your pet, can also cause allergic reactions like sneezing or a runny nose. Indoor allergies can be triggered by dust mites, mold, perfume and other irritants and also show themselves in runny noses and sneezing. This can be controlled by cleaning your house or apartment frequently (vacuum often) and changing out the air duct filters in shorter intervals. Once you find out what your baby is allergic to, it is manageable to avoid your baby suffering too much from it. When an allergy is confirmed, you can talk to your pediatrician about medication to bring relief to your baby from the symptoms. Cetirizine can be used in babies old enough to help them sleep if they are kept awake from their runny noses, sneezing or coughing.

In general, it is normal for babies to get sick and not a reason to be alarmed. Nevertheless, you should always follow your gut instinct. If you feel like something is wrong with your baby and there is a reason for them to be seen, then follow that instinct and take your baby in. It is always better to be discharged with a reassuring diagnosis of a common illness that will go away on its own after a few days, than something bad happening and looking back with regret that you didn't take them to be seen by a doctor. To care for your baby at home, set up a basic baby pharmacy with the most common medications or ointments you might need and feel comfortable using. Common and reliable ones are Tylenol, saline drops, Vaseline, thick body lotion, hydrocortisone, and diaper rash cream. Store all these items out of reach of your baby. To save time when you need to call a doctor, save the most important phone numbers in your phone like the pediatrician, nurse advice line, poison control line or the number of any other specialist your baby might be seeing. When it comes to your baby's wellbeing, you will always feel better and more relaxed when you are prepared for the eventualities. It is always best when you are well prepared and don't need to use medication or call the doctor.

Seeing your baby sick always makes you feel bad, but they will get stronger as a result, and they are resilient. Spoil your baby with some extra attention to comfort them and they will get better after a short time.

Memory Box

Notes of the First Time Baby is Sick

Picture of When Baby is Sick

Keep an Extra Band-aid From the First Pack of Band-aids

_____

_____

_____

_____

_____

_____

_____

_____

_____

_____

Difficulties Along the Way

The previous chapters focused on your pregnancy, the birth of your baby, and their first year, including milestones and important topics that come up during this time. Collectively, these chapters focused more on your new family. There are some difficulties along the way that happen in your changed environment that shape life around you. We will take a deeper look at them now.

Going through the experience of pregnancy to the first birthday of my first baby changed me. It also changed my view of the world around me. I always wanted to be the perfect mother to my child, the perfect wife to my husband, the perfect daughter to my mom, the perfect sister to my siblings, and the perfect friend. Trying to be the best for everyone around you usually means compromising and either putting yourself second, or getting someone angry. I used to be very flexible and not very set on how things needed to get done, therefore I did not mind catering to others more to try to make the best of any situation.

Becoming a mother and raising my daughters made me reflect on what it is I want to achieve and what my priorities are in life. Having children made it very easy for me to point out that my family came first, before everyone else around me. I learned to set boundaries and put my family first. I disappointed people around me whom I loved by saying no to them because it wasn't the best for my daughters, my husband, and me. It was difficult for me to accept this, but it was necessary. I lost old friends and made new friends. I learned to be selfish. In the end, it was the best for my family.

Before having children, we had friends we would frequently meet with for dinner and drinks that ended up in late night laughter until we all finally made it to bed by 3am. During my first pregnancy, we still continued that even though I didn't drink alcohol anymore. Once our first baby was born, our schedules changed with waking up at night, having to feed the baby, trying to get her to nap on a schedule during the day, then at night into bed on time and to sleep. Slowly but surely, we stopped hanging out and our invitations for outings and dinners vanished. Initially, it was difficult for me to understand why others would stop spending time with us when there was no argument or fallout between us, but over time, I learned to accept that people without little children might just not care for having babies who cry and interrupt unpredictably. Or maybe they just wanted to be supportive and understanding and give us the time and space we needed to figure things out, and didn't want to intrude. Whatever the reason, it was time to move on and not look back. Once you submerge yourself into the world of parenthood, you get exposed to other groups of parents around you and you find other people who understand your current situation and what you go through, and still happily spend time with you.

In general, you will encounter many situations where people around you will react in a different way than you expect, including complete strangers. This could be either in a positive or a negative way. You could get pushed aside by someone you considered a close friend, or you could find your biggest cheerleader in someone you have never met before. Whatever comes your way, be open-minded, take it for what it is and roll with it.

One major difficulty you have to deal with, if you are working, is the end of your maternity leave. It takes time to bond with your newborn and figure things out. By the time your maternity leave is over, your baby might still not be on a schedule, and may not be used to the bottle. You might still not feel 100% confident about how to handle your baby or fully comfortable in your role as a parent. Is it really possible you are now ready to trust someone else, a complete stranger most likely, with your baby? Some parents experience separation anxiety themselves and have a really hard time letting go of their little one. I most definitely felt like a bad parent and guilty when I sent my ten-month-old baby to daycare. It doesn't matter if your baby is twelve weeks or one year old; when you send them off, it is always difficult. You always want the best for your baby and you want things done your way. This is not how daycare works; you will always find something you will be critical of, no matter how great of a program it is.

However, there are also many developmental positives. Your baby will not be the center of attention and the main focus of the provider. Your baby is not the only one there and that is good- especially when they are older. Your baby will have to learn to share and to be patient. The good thing is usually when your baby is around others, they are curious and watch everyone, and want to learn whatever they can. They might not care that the focus is not on them all the time because there is enough other entertainment. In some children, this environment fosters more independent behaviors. Your baby will most likely learn things faster in daycare than at home because there are other children around they can imitate. Once you can find peace with yourself, keep it. No matter what daycare you choose and how great they are-or even if it is a nanny or au pair or a family member-you will always find something that bothers you in each installation and with each person that is not you. Learn to accept that. If you cannot compromise, then you will never be happy with anyone else but yourself taking care of your child.

Another added frustration is if your baby cries when you pick them up and they would rather stay at daycare than come home. From an emotional perspective, you want your baby to miss you and prefer being around you. Don't take it personally if your baby prefers daycare or asks to go there on the weekends. It means they have fun and have established a loving relationship based on trust with their provider. Interacting with their provider and the other children helps their development and social skills. They still know who their mom and dad are. They still love you the most, but 'they have made friends'. It is the best situation you could wish for.

With your baby going to daycare or just through everyday life interactions, your baby gets exposed to germs and will get sick.

That is always hard to see, but it also has other effects. Once both parents are back to work, the big question is: Who takes off if your baby is sick or daycare is closed for a holiday that your company doesn't give off? The fairest way would be if both parents took turns. Some companies are very flexible with arrangements, whereas others might be stricter, depending on the position you hold and the workload present. If one parent has a very important meeting or deliverable at work, it might make more sense for the other parent to take off. This is definitely a topic to discuss beforehand to ensure you are both on the same page and are not taken by surprise, fighting over whose work is 'more important' than the other. Referencing one parent's work more important than the other is not productive.

Don't undermine your partner's feelings, but take their work seriously, even if they make less money than you do. Everyone wants to be valued for their hard work. Many times, it is still expected for the mother to take time off work, no matter if it makes financial sense or not. If your employer seems to expect you as a mother to take off, it is ok for the partner to speak up and set expectations. Fathers are just as involved and responsible as the mothers. I experienced this the most when my husband was on active duty and I was 'just' the Military spouse, or dependent, as referred to in the military community. It didn't matter that I had a full-time job working on a project to validate the production equipment of the COVID-19 vaccine, to bring it to the market place and get people around the world vaccinated. Every day counted; people were dying. I still ended up taking the day off when our daughter was sick, working late nights to make up for some of the time lost while my husband had a normal working day. It didn't feel good, but it was the expectation of my husband's employer. Try to work around each other's schedules and support each other. Everyone's work is important.

Ultimately, if you have not developed thick skin by now, the perfect time is NOW, in order to deal with conflict properly. 'Properly' means that it has the least effect on you and your family. Just get through it and, no matter the outcome, take it and move on. This also includes friends and family. Everyone around you is used to you doing your own thing as an adult, who is not bound to any schedules and who can just do whatever they want, being spontaneous and flexible. This changes when you become a parent and need to figure out your child's schedule and keep their interest in mind. Especially if everyone around you is an adult and there are no other kids involved. You might be the first one in your circle of friends to have children, or bring the first grandchild into the family. People still plan things as they used to, when only adults were around, and this might not fit your life with a baby anymore. This can cause friction when you want to get together and suddenly cannot be the 'old you' anymore. Learn how to deal with conflict. If they don't understand your situation, then maybe they are not worth keeping around. Your baby and family come first; others need to understand that. If they take offense, then they don't have your best interest in mind, but only theirs. Is it worth putting your family second to their needs? That is something you have to decide for yourself.

You will probably lose some of your old friends, especially if they don't have children, because your lifestyle suddenly changes so dramatically. Don't take it personally. You did nothing wrong and don't try to force them to hang out with you. Not everyone enjoys having a crying baby around when they want to enjoy a drink and have a good time. In general, some people don't want children around and find them irritating. Some people cannot have children and it might be difficult for them to see you experiencing this miracle. You never know their side of the story, so take it as it is and move on. As sad as it is to lose friends, you will make new ones who support you and who might be at the same stage in life.

Another phenomenon that might really frustrate you is meeting many people who will discourage you rather than support you and cheer you on. They might even mean well and think they give you good advice. That's the last thing you need. You might hear how raising your baby with more than one language is so difficult and confusing. They will not understand anything, and will fall behind. It will be too much for them. This usually comes from people who either didn't have the opportunity to offer more than one native language to their children, or who failed to be consistent and didn't follow through, so it didn't work out for them. They are proven wrong when they see your toddler speaking more than one native language without a problem and believe they must be gifted in some way.

Another typical situation I have encountered mostly in the United States, is other moms encouraging you to stop breastfeeding.

Advice is given to feed your baby formula at the slightest sign of you struggling or when they hear breastfeeding is difficult. Of course, formula is also good and your baby will grow up just fine, but it is scientifically proven that breast milk is still the best option. Nobody said it will be easy, but it is worth figuring out and continuing. If you have a difficult time bringing up your milk supply, it is still better for you to feed your baby the breast milk you have, then supplement with formula, than to stop breastfeeding and switch to formula altogether. Try to find someone who is willing to listen to your difficulties and tries to support you working things out, cheering you on, and trying to solve the issue rather than tell you to quit right away. You might still get to the point where you decide to switch over to formula completely, but at least you tried it and will have a better conscience and be at peace with yourself. You don't want to look back and regret the choices you made because people around you were negative and unsupportive.

One of my friends experienced this discouragement when it was time to introduce solids to her baby. She wanted to cook her own food, but wasn't sure where and how to start. It is not always easy to find recipes with guidance on when to introduce what, when to move on to finger foods, what are good ingredients, and so on.

Friends and family around her were quick to tell her not to worry about cooking, but to rather buy the prepared baby food in jars because it would be more convenient and cheaper. As stated before, if this is the route you choose to go, great, there is delicious and healthy food out there for babies. But that is not the point here. It is about trying to discourage a mother who purposely chooses the more labor-intensive route to know exactly what her baby is eating. I always wonder why people are working so hard against what other parents actually want to do? Why can't they be happy for them and their choices, and do their best to support them? Try to find someone else who shares the same beliefs and interests and support each other. Exchange ideas and share what you learned with each other. Nobody knows everything and you don't always know best, so try to find the resources that really help to guide you. Talk to your pediatrician about any questions or doubts you have because they will tell you the most contemporary authoritative research, not what they deem to be easier for you. The things you value most are not necessarily the things others value. Also, it doesn't matter because you are the one raising your baby, not them. Be self-conscious, confident, and do your own thing.

Finally, one of the most difficult topics for the mothers: weight-loss or the new me? On mass media, you often see those super moms who shortly after giving birth have bounced back to a size zero, along with a six-pack! For some women with good genes, this is not a problem, especially after the first baby. I was one of those lucky ones. Naturally, I expected the same thing to happen after I had my second baby, but that was not the case. Even after I got a personal trainer six months after the delivery, started working out regularly, incorporated a protein shake into my diet, and cut out many of the unhealthy snacks, I had a difficult time seeing any difference. As you get older, your body doesn't recover as fast, and your body literally changes permanently during the process of pregnancy and giving birth. Your hips get wider. Your organs move around. Your bones literally move out of the way so you can push a baby out of you. There definitely are struggles in accepting your current body and finding the energy to do something about it if it bothers you. Many mothers put their families before themselves and their overall wellbeing, not investing in themselves. I learned you have to find that space and time for yourself where you will be selfish and do what you need to do to feel happy with yourself again. Some find it earlier, some find it later, but you will get to that point. Until then, embrace your new body because you had a baby, and that is amazing. It doesn't matter how others see you; it matters to have a supportive partner who appreciates you going through this physically traumatic experience to give them a child. Listen to your partner and believe them when they tell you that even with the added twenty pounds, you look amazing to them because you gifted them their child and that is the greatest gift they could ever ask for. It matters to have a partner who will support you with getting back to your old self, or to the point where you feel happy. Just keep in mind, getting back to your old self might look a little bit different from before because your body does change due to pregnancy and birth.

Once you accept there will be difficulties and changes in your life that you were not expecting, you can mentally prepare for them. Once they come your way, they won't shock you as much and you can deal with them better. Try to always remind yourself of what matters the most to you, what is the important goal, and what do you need to do to get there. Whenever a difficult situation comes up, take a step back, look at your baby and your partner and remember what is really important in your life. There will be difficulties along the way, but you will make it through them and come out to be a stronger and happier family.

Memory Box

Write Down the Difficulties. Your Baby Will Want to Know These Things When They Grow Up.

Keep a Memento from People Who Really Helped You Out.

Pictures of Supportive Friends/Groups

Write Down What Made You Happy

_____

_____

_____

_____

_____

_____

_____

_____

_____

_____

Some Final Words

Congratulations, you made it through the book!! You didn't close it and put it to the side because what I wrote was too much information to handle. You got a first glimpse of what having a baby and raising your newborn up to their first year will really be like. You read about the pregnancy, responsibilities, labor and delivery, the first six weeks after having the baby, the rest of the first year of your baby, and some difficulties along the way. We looked at the good, the bad, and the ugly together, and you should have a very good understanding of what is coming your way now.

For me, celebrating my daughter's first birthday was a huge milestone and made me reflect so much about the time spent together. I looked back and saw what I did well, but also where I lacked more patience or better knowledge to deal with the situations. It was the best year of my life, but also the hardest one. Being a first-time mother during my daughter's first year was the toughest challenge I've done in my life, but it also gave me the strength to go above and beyond with everything else in my life. Suddenly, anything else that came my way just seemed so much easier than raising a child. With my second baby, things were very different, some easier, and some harder. She didn't get the same one-on-one attention as my first one, but I did what I needed to do to keep the family happy. I have two wonderful daughters and I have become a better person thanks to them. I now look forward to going through this entire experience a third time, hopefully soon.

Reading this book means you are preparing for your baby and for yourself. This shows you care, and that is what is most important. Don't pressure yourself into being perfect. Be the best you can with all the values you want your children to have. I know at some points in this book, the horror stories took over the nice stories. Just keep in mind this book is specifically written to highlight the not so rosy parts of pregnancy, birth, and parenthood so you can prepare yourself better for what is coming your way. It is easy to find many resources that will tell you all the beautiful things about having a baby. This is why I found it so important to offer you the under-reported, or sometimes taboo perspective of the experience.

That being said, deciding to be a parent and going through everything we looked at in this book is the most wonderful and fulfilling experience you could ever wish for. Whatever you go through with your baby, whenever they look you deep in your eyes and start smiling, whenever they fall asleep on you because they completely trust you, makes it all worth it. The sleepless nights, the teething pain, and all the other discomforts your baby goes through will pass. Being a parent is forever and our greatest joy.

If you haven't done so yet, take some time for yourself, sit down and think about what is important for you to teach your baby and how you want to raise them. Then answer the question of what do you not want? Afterwards, sit down with your partner and discuss the different important topics so you will both be on the same page with how you want to raise your child.

Take some time for yourself to do what you truly enjoy and follow that with couple-time. Try to get as much rest as possible and enjoy the long hot showers and doing your hair. Go out for a leisurely, romantic dinner and enjoy each other.

This book was mainly based on my experiences and what I thought was the right thing to do with my babies. It does not mean that everything I did will work for you. You most likely will disagree with any number of things I brought up. That is perfectly fine. Take from this book what makes sense for you and don't worry about the rest. If you found something helpful, awesome! If you found everything to be exaggerated and not your style, that is OK, too. At least you know what you don't want for your children, and that is equally important. I just hope this book gives you the confidence and motivation to raise your baby the way you want, without caring about pleasing other people and without doubting yourself. I truly hope this book has helped you in finding some answers to your questions and in preparing you more for what lies ahead of you. I know some parts are scary and uncomfortable, but looking back, all of it will be worth it. Enjoy parenthood and make it your personal experience, not the one people around you tell you it should be. Be patient with yourself and trust your instincts.

Keep in mind whatever you do is amazing. Especially to your child. You will be their hero. They will love you unconditionally. You will be perfect to them.

Acknowledgments

My biggest thank you goes out to my supportive husband, who brought up the idea of me writing a book and sharing my experiences. Without his playful joking around, I would have not considered putting this together. Thank you for letting me trade in our couple-time for finishing this project.

Thank you to all my family and friends who believed in me, shared my excitement, and have been there for me when I got stuck during the writing process: my mom Kiki, my aunt Karen-Margrethe, my uncle Thomas, Danielle, Jordan, Sofie, Alma, Janina, and everyone else who has been there for me and encouraged me.

Thank you to the Self-Publishing School and the community, for all the help and insight, the feedback and motivation to make this a readable book. Seeing your passion, your success and your support has gotten me over writers block and has taught me so much about the writing process. My respect goes out to you.

Author Bio

Ann-Christin Villegas has a lifelong love for books. She never planned on writing one, but here we are. Becoming a mother and all the struggles that come with it literally opened a new chapter of her life. She is passionate about empowering other parents to pursue the vision they have for their family without giving into the easy way out and the peer pressure around them. She hopes this book is your no-nonsense go-to book when dealing with topics most people shy away from.

Originally from Friedberg, Germany, Ann-Christin resides in Northern Virginia with her husband Luis, two (for now) daughters Mila and Livia and two cats, Pubi and Panta. She is a PMP certified Biotech Engineer and works as a consultant in the pharmaceutical industry. She loves to travel, especially to Germany, where she was born and raised. She enjoys cooking and baking, followed closely by eating. Ann-Christin is always up for an adventure and likes scuba diving, just not with unexpected Bull Sharks encircling...but that is another story for another time.

URGENT PLEA

Thank You for Reading my Book!

Love this book? Don't forget to leave a review!

Every review matters, and it matters a *lot!*

Head over to Amazon or wherever you purchased this book to

leave an honest review for me.

I thank you endlessly.

Ann-Christin Villegas

Printed in Great Britain
by Amazon